What About my Kids?

A Guide for Parents Living with Breast Cancer

Linda J. Corsini, MSW, RSW

Table of Contents

Dedication

I have had the privilege of learning from many families who have lived with breast cancer, and I have witnessed their remarkable strength, endurance, and courage. This book is dedicated to them. I hope *What About My Kids?* communicates their wisdom to others who now face similar challenges.

I also dedicate this book to my mother Josephine Agro Corsini, to my mother-in-law Annette Denault Munt, and to my daughter Serena Corsini-Munt, from whom I learned what it means to be a mother.

Foreword

What About my Kids? is the name of a workshop for parents I have been leading at The Ottawa Hospital Regional Cancer Centre since 1996. Leading this workshop encouraged me to gather the wisdom that emerged from these group discussions into one resource for the benefit of all parents who are diagnosed with breast cancer.

With funding assistance in 2002 from the Canadian Breast Cancer Foundation, and with the multifaceted support of The Ottawa Hospital Regional Cancer, as well as community partners, this goal has now become a reality.

Sometimes we are asked by parents to help explain their breast cancer diagnosis to their children. We have found that, given the right tools to understand their condition, it is helpful for parents to share that information with their children themselves. Each family will have a unique approach to dealing with the situation, but we hope that this book is a useful guide.

The material presented in *What About my Kids?* is based on the genuine collaborative efforts of many people and organizations. Prior to publication, we held focus groups with our community partners to obtain feedback from women and men who are living with breast cancer. Many generously shared their stories, which have contributed to the pages that follow. Thank you for your spirit and care. This book was enriched because of your generosity.

Two Voices

Voices of parents with breast cancer

Jane

When Linda told me about her ideas for this book, I knew how important it would be. My mother died of breast cancer, I am a mother who has had breast cancer, and I carry a gene mutation which means that my children and I are at greater risk for developing certain cancers.

When my mother was diagnosed with cancer in 1968, my parents decided to protect us from what was happening. We knew she was sick, but we did not know what was wrong with her. Other people would talk quietly and whisper things behind our backs. We knew that something was terribly wrong. My five brothers and I handled our mother's illness and death differently. One of us withdrew, another became angry, and I developed a fear of abandonment.

When I heard my own diagnosis, I swore that I would be open and upfront with my children who were six and eight at the time. I wanted to include them in everything. I decided that I was an expert because I had been a child in similar circumstances. What I had yet to learn was that my kids were individuals, with their own personalities and their own ways of coping.

My youngest son reacted right away. He became afraid to let me out of his sight. At first, my oldest son took everything in stride, but a year later, as I was recovering, a child at school told him that when people have cancer, it always comes back and it always kills them. He, too, became afraid to let me out of his sight. Many people believe that this statement is true, but most people with breast cancer survive their disease. That is why it is important to understand what your child believes about your illness.

This resource would have helped my husband and me so much. We made mistakes, gave the children too much information, too much responsibility, and we let them get "lost in the shuffle." I needed help. I met with Linda who helped our family pull through, without any lasting negativity or hidden anger. She gave us our family back, and she strengthened our bonds by helping my husband and me hear what our children were saying.

I encourage you to read this book, use any and all available resources, and don't be afraid to ask for help. Your kids are the most important things in your life and they will suffer because of your illness. But you are not powerless. You can help them.

Jane Lorente Shepherd

Christine

My journey with breast cancer spans over 22 years, from 1983 to 2005 and has been a challenging and wondrous journey. I hope that my experiences can help give you the hope and encouragement that you need at this time.

My ability to survive comes from hope, trust, a sense of humour, a positive attitude, realistic priorities, learning how to say no, and facing life head on. Singing, watching funny movies, and partying have helped me and, by default my family, enormously.

My experiences haven't always been positive, though. "What an awful legacy for my girls," I wept as my surgeon told me that I had another recurrence of breast cancer – my eighth since my first diagnosis in 1983.

I was first diagnosed in June 1983 at age 37 when "cancer" was a word that was spoken in hushed tones and that was not discussed openly. My diagnosis terrified my husband and two pre-teen children and shocked me. Between 1983 and 1988, I had five recurrences. Then, in 1994 the cancer came back once again. Seven years later, in 2001, I had another recurrence in both breasts. 2003 and 2004 brought recurrences in my neck, my left side, and my spine.

My children were 10 and 12 years old when I was diagnosed and they lived through my many hospitalizations and treatments at a particularly vulnerable time in their young lives. Because my immediate family was overseas, my amazing friends, a wonderful oncologist, social worker, as well as doctors and nurses, became my extended family of choice. Even with this extended family, I often had the responsibility of providing reassurance and support to my own family. A resource such as this one would have been a godsend to me and my family at that time.

Support groups were few and far between in the 1980s and it was more difficult to gain access to information. I was lucky to live in an urban area where treatment was easily available, but I met many women, some very young, who had to leave their homes and children for months at a time because there were no facilities in their area. They too could have used such a resource.

My daughters Alison and Samantha are now 32 and 34, and my most recent recurrences affect them in a more meaningful way. They are now much closer to the same age that I was when I was diagnosed. My husband, Richard, a wonderful, kind, and compassionate soulmate of 12 years, has been through nearly as many recurrences as my ex-husband, Philip, who is still a great friend.

I have gained many positive things through my journey with breast cancer. I now take time for myself and enjoy my wonderful and amazing daughters. Although we live in different cities and countries, we spend as much time together as we can and we visit often by phone or e-mail. Our roles have changed, and in many ways, they mother me. They too are survivors. They have grown into sensitive, caring, compassionate, and beautiful young women who have learned from my diagnosis of breast cancer to enjoy each and every moment of their lives.

To my great friends and supporters – you all know who you are – I couldn't have come so far without you. To Richard, Alison, and Samantha, I offer you my love and gratitude for being so blessed to have you in my life.

To all of you going through the fight – hang in, love, laugh, and celebrate life!

Christine Sones

Introduction

When parents are diagnosed with breast cancer, the first question that many of them ask is "Am I going to die?" The second question that they ask is "What about my kids?"

When you learn that you have breast cancer, it is natural to be concerned about your children. Breast cancer affects you, your children, and your entire family. As a parent, part of the challenge of living with breast cancer is how to balance your own needs with those of your children. Facing this challenge and finding ways to cope with parenting is not easy. However, you cannot stop parenting while you are dealing with breast cancer; your children still need to be parented.

"What about my kids?"

This resource book offers information about your needs while you are living with breast cancer, as well as those of your children. Changes will be necessary in your family's life. This book can help you recognize when you can make changes and how to make them. Families live with cancer not only during treatment, but also during survivorship. Even if your cancer is treated successfully and is in remission, its effects can remain and alter your outlook on life and your parenting style. Life might not be the same as it was before you had breast cancer.

What About My Kids? is written primarily for parents with breast cancer. It can also be helpful for parents with any form of cancer or life threatening disease. The book can also benefit the support partner of someone with cancer. A support partner can be any caring adult who shares parenting responsibilities, such as another parent, the partner of the parent with cancer, a family member, or a close friend who has a loving and guiding relationship with the children. Your family can consist of the people who are related to you, but the definition of family can also include those people who you are close to by choice. You might look to several people to share the role of support partner. This book might also be helpful for others who have relationships with the children, such as childcare providers, teachers, and the parents of your children's friends.

No two families are alike, and families constantly change. Families differ in cultural background, in geographic location, and in spiritual beliefs. This book acknowledges and respects such differences, as well as the diverse ways that people and families cope with serious illness. The term children refers to sons and daughters of all ages, including adult children who are also affected by their parent's illness.

The majority of people survive breast cancer. Some do not. Survival rates are increasing year by year and, for some, breast cancer becomes a chronic illness that presents specific challenges for families. Yet, the fear of recurrence and the fear of dying are common to most parents who are diagnosed with this disease. For these reasons, *What About My Kids?* discusses the entire course of the illness, so that it can offer information, ideas, and resources for all parents with breast cancer. You may choose to read the entire book or only select the chapters that apply to your situation. Some later chapters like: "Advancing Illness and Dying" and "Death and Grieving" may be emotionally difficult to read.

This book is not intended as a how-to manual with the right answer for every challenge. Every family and individual is unique and will experience circumstances beyond the scope of this book.

Parents know their own children best. Take what you need from this book and trust yourself and your instincts. It is natural and common for parents to worry about their children when a parent is diagnosed with breast cancer, regardless of how old their children are. Managing these concerns and communicating with your children during your illness are the basic themes of this book.

Parenting Through Breast Cancer

What children need from a parent with breast cancer

Parenting is a difficult job during the best of times, but if you are ill, parenting can seem overwhelming. When you have breast cancer, balancing your own needs with those of your children might be the most difficult experience that you and your support partner encounter in your lives. However, for the health and wellbeing of your entire family, it is important for you to maintain a strong relationship with your children when you are ill.

Children need both roots and wings.

At any time, the fundamentals of successful parenting can be described as providing children with both "roots" and "wings."

Roots grow when children are loved and cared for and when they feel as though they belong, are secure, safe, and contribute to their family. When you have breast cancer, you can help your children feel rooted by providing several things:

- A regular routine and family life, by keeping consistent meals, bedtimes, school hours, and extracurricular activities

- Information about what is happening with the family

- Reassurance that they will always be cared for

- Continued support and understanding

Wings develop when parents foster their children's sense of self and individual personalities, and when they help them develop skills and knowledge that enable them to become independent. Parents can encourage independence by communicating with their children, by setting boundaries, and by exposing them to age-appropriate information and experiences. When you have breast cancer, you can help your children develop wings by providing several things:

- Continued support of their independence
- Encouragement to take time away from the family so that they can maintain a sense of self
- Preservation of their regular interests or activities away from home
- Appreciation for how they are coping with the family situation

When you are healthy, parenting successfully can be challenging, and when you are living with breast cancer, it can be even more difficult to provide your children with both the roots and the wings that they need.

Why communicating with your children about breast cancer is important

Open communication between family members is important at any time, but it is essential when a parent has a serious illness. There is no easy way to tell your children that you have breast cancer and no parent wants to experience this. Part of the parenting role is to protect children from harm, and you may choose to protect your children from knowing about your diagnosis for as long as possible, because you think it will hurt them. It is understandable to want to protect your children from worrying about your health and the future.

"If you're not honest, kids will imagine all kinds of scenarios and what they imagine can be far worse than the truth."

However, children are better able to cope with a parent's serious illness if they are given information clearly and honestly. They will manage all aspects of your illness better if you are open with them than if you withhold information.

Children are very perceptive and can often sense more than they can express, such as a parent's stress or discomfort. Not talking does not protect your children from the reality that something serious is happening. By keeping information from them, you can prevent your children from making sense of what they see and feel. In fact, when children do not know what is happening, they can develop misunderstandings or imagine explanations of what they observe.

Children of all ages will fill in information that they do not have with their own logic and imagination, and their interpretations could be much worse than the reality. Even if the information that you have is not positive, it is easier for your children to deal with the truth instead of rumours and misinformation.

Children can often sense when something is not right, but they might not know what to say or how to address it. Children need help and direction to discuss a parent's illness and they need to know that it is okay to talk about their feelings. If you are open and approachable, you can help encourage your children to express their feelings and questions.

Often during this period, family members can develop closer and stronger ties to one another.

You can strengthen your relationship with your children even during a health crisis.

Communicating and giving your children age-appropriate information about your breast cancer can build and strengthen the relationship between you and your children.

Talking to your children about breast cancer can help them cope better. Your children can adjust better to the changes in your family life during your illness if they understand how breast cancer and its treatment will affect them. They will also feel reassured that they will continue to be cared for.

Breast cancer can be cured, or it could become a chronic or even life-threatening illness. If your breast cancer becomes a chronic illness, it will require ongoing adjustments from your family. Children can adapt more easily to these adjustments if they are informed about and expect them from the beginning.

You are a model for your children on how to deal with your illness. Being open and honest helps your children respond in the same way. Being honest with your children also promotes and builds trust between you and helps preserve closeness, particularly during your illness. As children grow, parents have to trust their children's judgment and ability to cope with crises or unforeseen circumstances. Surprisingly, children can often react better than you expect.

How to communicate with your children about breast cancer

How you communicate with your children about your breast cancer depends on several factors:

- Your readiness and level of openness
- Your individual style of communication
- Your children's ages and stages of development
- Your children's unique personalities
- The seriousness of your illness
- Your unique family situation
- Your cultural practices
- Your spiritual beliefs

Honesty is the best policy

As you prepare to talk to your children, the following communication guidelines might help.

1. Prepare yourself

Understand the medical information before you tell your children

You might find it helpful to wait until you receive test results, so that you can share information in a clear and informed manner. If you choose to tell your children before you have all the information, reassure them that you will give them information when you have it.

Plan *who* will talk to your children

The person who has the closest relationship with your children is often the best person to share information with them about your cancer. Ideally, you and your support partner will share your breast cancer diagnosis with your children. If you have differing views from your support partner about what to communicate, you should discuss your differences and decide together how to proceed. Any information that your children receive about your breast cancer should be consistent so that they are not confused. If you want help communicating specific information, you can also ask for help from your health care team.

Plan *when* to talk to your children

You should choose a time to communicate with your children when you feel able, rested, and ready. There is never an ideal time to share difficult news, but your child is more likely to listen when you are out for a walk, a drive, tucking them into bed, or washing the dishes together, for example. You should also ensure that when you communicate, you will have enough time to answer any questions that your children have.

Plan *where* to talk to your children

You might not always have the choice about where to communicate with your children, because they might ask questions at any time. If you can choose a location, choose somewhere that feels safe and comfortable for both you and your children.

2. Communicate openly

Communicate with children on their level

Provide information according to your child's ability to understand. You might want to talk to each of your children individually so that you can speak at their level of maturity and to their individual personalities. If you discuss your breast cancer with all of your children, target your explanation to the youngest child. You can provide additional information to your older children later.

Be brief

Be clear and use correct words. Share information a little at a time to avoid information overload. Your children might stop listening or might not be able to understand if there is too much information. Your children's behaviour will usually show when they have had enough. You are the best judge of how much information to share.

Be honest

Try not to give your children guarantees or make false promises to them. False expectations can easily create disappointment and a sense of failure. Life has no guarantees. You will have a strong desire to tell your children that everything will be alright, but you should resist giving them false assurances. If you have reason to be upbeat and positive, then share the news in this way. If you have reason to worry about your future, then try to be clear and stay close to the medical information that you have. If you do not know the answer, say so. Tell them you will find out and give them the information as soon as possible. Focus on keeping your communication honest.

Listen carefully

Listen to your children to understand what they are asking and not asking. Try to be available and sensitive to any changes in their behaviour at home or at school.

Encourage feedback

Ask your children if they understand what you are telling them and let them tell you in their own words what they understand. Encourage your children to ask questions, and if they have them, try to answer them honestly. It is okay to say, "we don't know yet" or "the doctor is checking it out." If you can't answer their questions immediately, let them know when you will have the information.

Provide ongoing updates

Your children will need periodic and regular updates, even if nothing has changed. Even older children might need to hear information more than once to fully understand it or to feel reassured. Regular updates are important. You should continue to communicate with your children if your health changes or stays the same. Communicating once is not enough.

3. Be positive

Acknowledge your children's strengths in coping with your diagnosis

Give compliments and positive feedback when you observe your children helping around the house or doing tasks that they normally leave for you. Sometimes, children will respond well if you give them a job to do so that they feel as though they are helping.

Encourage children to express their feelings and thoughts about regular life and activities

Share the highs and lows of your day and invite them to do the same. Do not let cancer dominate your family life.

Let children be children

Offer your children time and space away from the rest of the family. Encourage your children to take time for themselves. Let your children know that it is okay to keep acting like a child.

Encourage play and leisure activities

Regular play has many benefits. Physical activity provides an outlet for venting feelings and creative play helps children express feelings and make sense of the world around them.

Apply humour to your illness

Try to laugh. Humour, especially in times of crisis, can be healing. Making jokes or finding humour in unlikely situations can relieve stress and tension for everyone. Your humour might encourage your children to make jokes too. Create happy times with your family.

4. Cope with fear for the future.

Lead by example

Understandably, your cancer diagnosis might make your children worry about the future. This concern is normal for both children and parents. It might be difficult, but try to manage your own feelings at this time so that you do not overwhelm your children. If you are overwhelmed, tell your children how you feel and that, for this reason, you are asking your support partner to help out until you feel more balanced. Show your children positive ways to cope. Talk about the future, and share your own feelings.

Take time out

Offer relief from the seriousness of their fears by taking time away from talking and thinking about it. Use distraction, watch a favorite movie, go for a walk, or invite a friend over for a visit.

Be available

Try to be available to your children physically, by spending time with them, and emotionally, by paying attention to them and showing that you understand and accept their feelings. Hug your children and give them special attention by telling them you love them.

5. Offer hope.

Everyone needs hope for the future. Your children need to know that they will be okay. Being sick with breast cancer will reduce your ability to parent as usual. Explain this to your children. If you cannot care for them, ensure that your support partner or another caring adult will care for them. Let them know that life will go on and that you expect they will go forward with their own job of attending school and growing up.

What to expect from your children when you communicate about breast cancer

Children will react differently to the news of your breast cancer according to their age, their stage of development, their personality, and your family circumstances. However, there are several reactions that you should expect.

"Everyone reacts differently."

Expected reactions

Silence

When you communicate with your children about such serious topics, silences are common. If a silence makes you uncomfortable, you might ask: "What are you thinking about?" Children might not know what to say or ask. Respect their need for time to absorb the information. Allow the silence without the need for anyone to talk.

Denial

Children naturally hope and look for signs that you are better and that everything will be alright, even if you are not well. This does not mean that they have not heard what you have communicated, although it might appear as if they are denying the facts. You and your support partner and adult family might also find it difficult to face the reality of your illness. It takes time for everyone to adjust.

Emotional responses

It is normal for your children to be sad, angry, scared, worried, and even to feel guilty. If your children express these types of feelings about your breast cancer, let them know that you too share these feelings. You could say, "We both feel sad." Joining your children in this way prevents them from keeping thoughts and emotions inside and encourages them to share their feelings with you. If your children appear troubled, you could reflect their feelings and say, "You seem worried or upset, am I right?"

Embarrassment

Some children experience embarrassment when their parent has breast cancer. They might not want to be viewed differently from others, and they might not be ready to discuss your illness openly yet. They might not be mature enough yet to handle messages of support and caring from others. It is normal for some school-aged children to not discuss their parent's illness with peers.

Troubling behaviour

Your children might already have behaviour problems that have little or no connection to your breast cancer. On the other hand, your health crisis might cause disturbances for your children.

Some children have a difficult time dealing with the chronic nature of a parent's breast cancer, which can span a period of years with many ups and downs. A drawn-out illness and treatment period require additional adjustments for children while they mature from childhood into adolescence, for example.

Signals of disturbances might be evident at home, school, or with other caregivers. You know your own children best and you and your support partner can often distinguish when your children's behaviours are normal and when they become troubling. If you are concerned about your children's behaviours, you should discuss them with your health care team. Counseling can help.

The following behaviours might signal that your children are having problems.

Regression

Children might start acting younger than their age or revert to earlier behaviours. For example, a young child who is toilet trained might start to have accidents. Young children might return to security objects that they gave up, such as a blanket or stuffed animal. Play patterns might change to a more solitary or introverted type of play, and children's artwork might demonstrate ways in which they are trying to make sense of what is happening.

Your child might want to be closer to you, return to the parental bed, or refuse to go to school. Grades might drop and teachers might alert you to problems at school. Older children and youth can also become more demanding and appear less capable and independent than before. Adolescent and adult children who were mature might now show signs of not coping by being tearful, staying away from home, or by not calling or visiting.

Handle this behaviour with tolerance and reassurance. Investigate the behaviour and discuss with your children what you observe.

Anger or acting out

Anger is a very legitimate and expected emotion when a parent becomes ill. Family routines change and the whole family can feel vulnerable. Your children's expectations and needs might conflict with what you and your support partner can offer. This conflict can produce frustration and anger, which might surprise you if you expect your children to become more understanding and accepting. Your children might become aggressive, and lash out at home, at playmates, or at you, by being defiant and oppositional. If this behaviour is out of character, it can signal that your children are hurting inside.

This behaviour can be difficult to deal with, especially when you have limited energy. Inviting your children to talk out feelings and to redirect this energy might help. However, your children need to know that there is a limit to how they can express their anger. Defining the limits is another way of letting your children know that there are boundaries for expressing feelings and for living together. Defining boundaries can provide security at a time of uncertainty, which is a responsibility that you and your support partner can share.

The quiet or "too good" child

Some children might react by trying to do everything to help, almost giving up their own activities to be helpful at home. These children might take on more responsibility for younger siblings, take charge of more housework, or study harder at school to get good grades to please parents. Encourage your children to continue with his or her own activities as much as possible. There is a danger that your children can take on a parenting role that is beyond their emotional and physical years. You and your support partner must define the limits and what you expect from your child as well as what the adult roles will be. Defining roles provides security and makes it easier for your children to act their real or appropriate age.

Anxiety and depression

Your children might talk about their own fear of dying and they might speak directly about their fear of losing you to cancer. They might gain or lose a significant amount of weight. Your children might seem overly sad, nothing might seem to make them happy, and they might lose interest in normal activities. They might have difficulty falling asleep or staying asleep. Listen to your children's comments and observe their behaviour. If you sense that your children are anxious or depressed, respond seriously and sensitively. Offer your children support and talk to your health care team to seek help.

Getting support for communicating with your children about breast cancer

With information, support, and resources, you can better deal with the concerns of your children during your illness.

Take advantage of all the sources of support that are available to you:

"Help is out there."

- Partner or support person
- Family and friends
- Cancer support groups
- Complementary therapies, such as meditation, diet, and exercise
- Spiritual and cultural communities

You might experience communication problems with your children when you are dealing with your breast cancer. It is your responsibility as a parent to talk about what is happening with your children. Use your best judgment. If you don't know how to start communicating or have reached an impasse, you can seek professional help from the following resources:

- Cancer Centre counseling services
- Family physician or health care team
- Local chapter of the Canadian Cancer Society

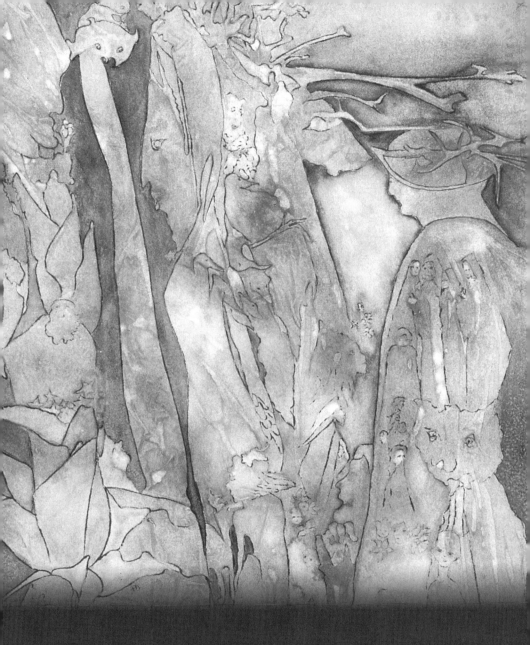

Diagnosis

Taking Care of Yourself

✤ *What to expect*

You have breast cancer.

No one can ever be prepared for the news that they have breast cancer and hearing a diagnosis is always upsetting. The shock of your diagnosis might keep you from hearing everything else that your doctor says about your illness during that visit. This is normal, and it is natural to feel shocked, upset or sad when you are diagnosed.

When you first hear the news, you might feel vulnerable and uncertain about your future. At this time, it is very important to remember that although some people with breast cancer will die from it, many more people receive treatment and survive.

Your breast cancer diagnosis and treatment can affect you in several ways. Most parents when confronted with a diagnosis of breast cancer ask:

"I sat there in a daze, comprehending nothing except the doctor's first words, 'You have cancer'."

- Will I die from my illness?

- What about my kids?

Other common questions parents have are :

- How will my partner manage with less help from me?

- What treatment will I have?

- How will I manage the side effects of treatment?

- How will my children deal with the side effects of my treatment?

- I live far away from a Cancer Centre. Where will I stay during treatment?

- How long will I have to be away from my family for treatment?

- Will I be able to continue to work or still pay my bills?

After your diagnosis, you might have times when you feel strong, and other times when you feel weak and upset. You might find yourself wanting to cry when you are with your family. This reaction is understandable and normal, and can show your children that it is okay to have emotional responses.

Breast cancer is a different illness for each person who has it. There are several types of breast cancer, and it is important for you to understand what type and stage of breast cancer that you have. For example, your breast cancer could be in one of the following stages:

- **Stage 0:** Very early or "in situ"

- **Stage 1:** Localized, with no spreading

- **Stage 2 or 3:** Some localized spreading into lymph nodes, such as lymph nodes in your armpit

- **Stage 4:** Metastases, where the cancer has spread to other parts of the body

You are unique. Your diagnosis, treatment, and specific situation can be different from anyone else's. Your reaction to your diagnosis can be unique as well.

❖ What to do

Seek information from your physician to help you understand what type and stage of breast cancer you have. Try to stay focused on the medical

"Before I could tell my kids, I had to figure it out myself first."

information you are being given, and not to worry about things that may or may not come later. Don't be afraid to ask questions of your physician and health care team.

Knowledge is power. Understand your diagnosis and learn as much as you can about it. The more that you understand what is happening to you, the better prepared you will be to deal with it. You have breast cancer, but you also have choices. Your illness and treatment will be less surprising and upsetting the more that you understand it.

If you are unsure about what questions to ask, the following can help get you started:

- What type of breast cancer do I have?

- What kind of treatment do I need?

- What are the side effects of my treatment?

- How long will the treatments last?

- How much time will I need to be away from work?

- What are my chances of survival?

After your diagnosis, the following suggestions might help you manage any further medical information that you receive:

- Start a notebook where you can keep your medical information and appointments.

- Bring a support person to all medical appointments when you discuss treatment plans or decisions. Another person can provide a second set of eyes and ears to help you better understand your options and to discuss them.

- Write down your questions and bring them to your medical appointments.

Getting Support

✤ What to expect

When you are diagnosed with breast cancer, you will need both medical and emotional support. The medical support that is immediately available to you might be influenced by where you live and your emotional support might be influenced by how many close family members and friends are around you. You might be part of a small or large family, or you might be isolated with few emotional supports for yourself and your children. Remember that you can choose your emotional supporters. You can decide to confide in and rely on the people that you care about. Remember that different people might be able to help you in different ways. When you receive support from others, both you and your children will feel that you are part of a larger community and that you are not alone.

When you are diagnosed with breast cancer, you should identify a support partner and ask that person if they are comfortable assuming that role. Your support partner will be the closest person to you during your time of need, and you will rely heavily on this person. Your support partner might be your spouse, friend, or relative. You might share the role with several people. Your support partner will be the main person that you go to for help and emotional support.

Just as it is an emotional experience for a parent who is diagnosed with breast cancer, it is also an emotional experience for the support partner. Support partners will also experience emotional highs and the lows throughout your diagnosis, illness, and treatment.

"I could not repeat the words 'I have cancer'; I needed someone to help me share the information with my kids."

The following points are important to remember about your support partner:

- Support partners might have different reactions and coping mechanisms than you do.

- You have to be realistic about what you can expect from a support partner, as everyone has needs and limits.

- Your support partner might experience caregiver stress. In addition to supporting you during your illness, your support partner will likely be responsible for more family, parenting, and household duties than before.

- A support partner should be able to ask for support as well as give it. Support partners might not feel as though they have a right to ask for help because they are not sick, but your relationship will best survive if it includes both giving and receiving, even during a health crisis such as breast cancer.

- Support partners must take time to focus on their own needs. Support partners should take care of their own health, and continue regular activities as much as possible. These activities will provide emotional space to lessen their physical and emotional fatigue. The ability of support partners to care for someone else depends on how well they take care of themselves.

�֍ *What to do*

Discuss with your support partner what you think your diagnosis of breast cancer means for you and your family. It is not unusual for parents and support partners to differ in comfort levels, readiness, and the ability to deal with breast cancer. Recognize your differences and deal with them as best you can.

"My partner dealt with the news of my cancer very differently than I did. He wanted to tell the kids right away and I wanted time to process the information on my own, before sharing it with the kids. So we had to compromise."

Parents aim to give children the tools that they need to be well-adjusted adults. Having loving relationships with other caring adults in their lives, in addition to their parents, can help children mature. Other adults can increase your children's sense of stability while you have breast cancer, because you might not be available to your children all the time during your illness. Look to your support partner and other caring adults to take on some parenting tasks. If you are a single parent, try strengthening and developing your networks through family, friends, or your health care team in the wider community.

Decide which other adults, such as caregivers or teachers, and parents of your children's closest friends, that you want to inform about your breast cancer diagnosis. Informing other adults can relieve your children from having to share the information themselves. It can be helpful to inform school staff of the situation at home. This will allow your child's teacher to keep a more vigilant eye if problems occur at school. Ask your children if their teachers are aware of the situation. Older children might not want you to share this information with certain people, and you should respect any appropriate wishes for privacy, as your diagnosis is sensitive and confidential information.

Communicating with your Children

❧ What to expect

Your breast cancer diagnosis affects you but it also directly affects your children. It is normal for both of you to feel sad, angry, and worried. Starting to communicate about such a serious

"It's natural to have a selfish reaction from your kids. My 13-year-old daughter's first thoughts were 'it's not fair' and 'what about me?'"

issue can be difficult, especially because having cancer introduces a whole new vocabulary.

Cancer is a powerful word and a difficult concept to understand. Most people lack the vocabulary to explain cancer in simple terms. Sometimes the word "cancer" is so shocking that when people hear it, they are unable to hear anything else. Adults usually have a stronger negative reaction to the word cancer than children do. Depending on your children's age, they might or might not have an idea of what the word cancer means.

When parents are diagnosed with a possible life threatening illness such as breast cancer, their first question is often "What about my kids?" When children hear the same news, they often ask "What about me?" Children depend on parents for care and nurturing, so it is normal for them to be concerned about themselves. If you are ill, they will worry about who will take care of them, if you cannot. Children may find it difficult that you've become the centre of attention and that people pay more attention to you than them (eg. their grandparents).

Telling children not to worry usually does not help. Your children might think that having cancer means that you're going to die. If you have cancer, anticipate that your children might assume this. You might have thought about this possibility and likely so have they. Allow your children to speak about this fear. If you believe that your children are thinking about this, but are not able to express it, you can ask them if they ever worry that you could die from your breast cancer and if they want to talk about it. Explain that you want to live as long as possible and that you and your health care team are doing your best so that you will get better.

Keep in mind that children are resilient. They have the ability to understand and cope. Your children will be able to deal with most news if you present it in an appropriate way. They can manage and cope with a situation if they understand what is happening, and if they know that they will be cared for during your illness.

The following questions and concerns are common when children learn that a parent has breast cancer:

Changes to routines and responsibilities

- Who will take care of us when you are sick?
- Who will drive me to school or my sports events?
- Will I have extra chores?

Concerns about your and their health

- Will you die?
- What will happen to us if you die?
- Can I get cancer too?

❖ What to do

Get in touch with your feelings before you talk with your children. Managing your own feelings about your diagnosis of breast cancer will better prepare you to explain your illness to your children. You are a role model for your children, and their responses will be influenced greatly by your reaction to and presentation of the information.

Take some time for you and your support partner to gather your thoughts before you share the news. During the time that you take to process the information, ask those who know not to talk about your diagnosis to your children, or in their presence, until you and your support partner have discussed it with your children first.

Seek help from the counselors at your Cancer Centre to prepare you for telling your children about your diagnosis. Remember that parents know their children best. You can get ideas and

"There is no such thing as doing a bad job telling your kids about your cancer. We do the best that we can. If you mess up the first time – you can go back and try again."

suggestions from outside sources, but only you can decide what will work best for your family.

When you are ready to communicate your diagnosis to your children, these guidelines might help:

- Decide what you will tell your children.

- Prepare what you want to say.

- Choose a location that feels safe and secure.

- Gather everyone that you want to be there.

- Try to manage your feelings as best as you can.

- Use simple, clear, and accurate language.

- Try to convey a consistent message.

- Be honest about what you know.

- Give age-appropriate information.

- Do not give too much information at one time.

- Ask if they understand.

- Encourage questions.

- Listen to feedback.

- Reassure your children that they will be cared for.

The most basic way to communicate your diagnosis is to start with a simple statement such as "I went to see my doctor and she told me that I have breast cancer. It is a serious illness and I will need treatment for it."

Sometimes, adolescents or young adult children prefer to get the information from someone other than their parent such as a member of the health care team. Invite them to discuss your diagnosis with a member of your health care team.

Questions and Answers

It is natural for children to have questions and to ask, or avoid asking, some difficult ones. The following sample questions and answers can give you an idea of how to approach some common questions.

- **What is cancer?**

  Our bodies are made up of millions of cells that all have their own jobs to do. When a person has cancer, some of those cells change and grow out of control. The cancer cells take over some parts of your body where healthy cells should be. The "unhealthy" or cancer cells grow together and make a lump or tumour.

- **How did you get cancer?**

  No one really knows why some people get cancer and others don't. This makes it very difficult to understand. People who research cancer are also still not completely sure why. They continue to work on finding the reasons why a healthy cells turns cancerous.

- **Did I cause the cancer?**

  No. Nothing anyone did caused this cancer or can make it worse. You do not have the ability to cause someone to get cancer. We are not sure why I have cancer and someone else does not.

- **Will I get cancer?**

  Cancer is not contagious. You cannot catch cancer. You can touch me and hug me without any problem. There are many reasons why people get cancer. Just because your parent has it does not mean you will get it too.

- **Can I avoid getting cancer?**

  There are some things that you can do that might help reduce the possibility of cancer or other illnesses:

  - Take proper care of yourself.
  - Have regular check-ups with your doctor.
  - Eat a healthy diet.
  - Stay active.
  - Do not smoke.
  - Drink alcohol in moderation.

- **How do people with cancer get better?**

  Cancer can be treated in different ways. The normal treatment options include:

  - Surgery
  - Chemotherapy (a treatment which uses one or more drugs to destroy cancer cells)
  - Radiotherapy

Diagnosis

Common concerns	• Shock and disbelief • Health crisis for entire family • Telling your children about your cancer might be the most difficult task that you face • Emotional and physical needs are high
Parent with cancer	• Worry about self, partner, and children • Loss of control over one's life
Support partner	• Similar concerns as partner with cancer
Children	• Need for information that is appropriate for their age and interest level • Knowledge of what is happening and how their parent's illness and treatment affect their lives • Belief in the competence of their parents to survive a health crisis
Coping tips	• Keep open and clear communication with your support partner • Spell out what you need and expect from each other. • Be open and honest with your children • Take the lead to build dialogue and share your progress and updates. • Seek out help for yourself and them if needed. • Learn new language & vocabulary to share information • Stay connected, open and honest • Contain anxiety • Be forgiving: this is not your fault

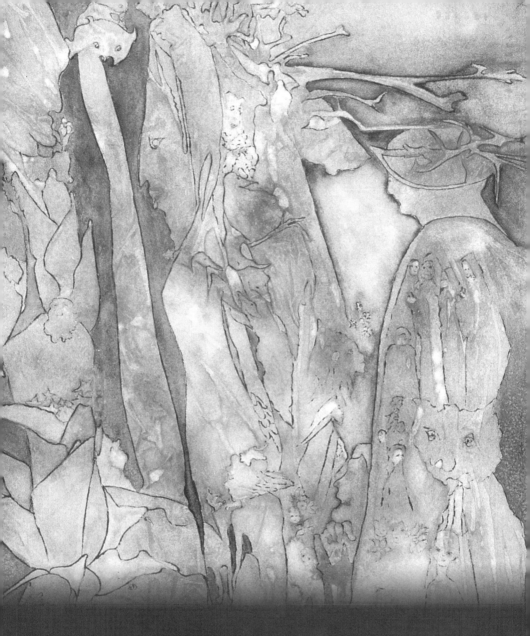

Treatment

Treatment

Taking Care of Yourself

❖ What to expect

Regardless of what kind of treatment you receive for your breast cancer, it will change your day-to-day family life. You will be required to attend many treatment appointments, and when your treatment starts, your regular routines will change. The changes to your family life might happen slowly or quickly. You might experience few disruptions or you might feel a loss of control over your life. Your treatment can cause disruptions to routine, increased demand on family responsibilities, and reduced finances, all of which can be stressful.

You might try hard to keep your life as normal as possible, but you should expect that some level of change will happen. Your energy levels will not be the same. Try to be flexible and patient with yourself and your family members as you all adjust to the new circumstances.

Treatment for breast cancer varies for each individual. You might have surgery, chemotherapy, radiation, or a combination of these. Treatment of any kind can affect the following aspects of your life:

- Your physical presence at home

- Your emotional availability at home

- Your energy levels

- Your physical appearance

"You need to find the strength to go on and don't give up hope."

- Your ability to work both inside and outside your home

You might also experience several of the following side effects from your treatment:

- Nausea
- Pain and discomfort
- Fatigue
- Difficulty concentrating
- Forgetfulness
- Hair loss
- Weight loss or gain

❖ *What to do*

Be active in your treatment. Do your own research and ask lots of questions. Enlist someone to help you with your research so that you can ask your doctors questions to fully understand your options. Knowledge can help you make the best use of your health care team and being informed can help you feel more in control of your treatment. Try as much as possible to understand the medical information, advocate for yourself, and be assertive about what you do and do not want and need.

If you experience unpleasant side effects from your treatment such as uncontrollable nausea discomfort, seek medical help. Bring your side effects to the attention of your health care team so that you can receive the appropriate pain and symptom-management control.

Throughout your treatment, try to keep your expectations realistic. Your usual capacity to parent will be reduced. Accept that your energy levels will not be the same, and that you will not be able to maintain your normal level of functioning. When you are ill, you might unintentionally expect

"Taking care of yourself is the best way to take care of your kids."

more of yourself than your health or energy level allows. Similarly, you might expect more from your partner or your children than they can provide. Strive for balance and lower your expectations about what you can and cannot do.

Take time to care for yourself throughout your illness. Taking care of yourself might be something as simple as taking the time to go for a walk, listen to your favourite music, visit with friends, go for lunch, or watch a movie. Taking care of yourself can help you cope with what you are experiencing, and can help refresh your energy and your mood. Take time away from treatment and household routines to nurture and be good to yourself. Taking care of yourself can also help lessen your children's worry about you.

Getting Support

❋ *What to expect*

As you receive treatment for your breast cancer, you will have reduced energy for your usual role as a parent. As a result, your support partner will likely assume more parenting tasks than before. If you are a single parent, other adults might assume some of your parenting jobs.

Depending on your individual situation, finding and receiving support might be difficult. Regardless of your situation, seek support. It is never easy to ask for help, and often you might not know where to go or who to ask. Sometimes, people might offer their support, but do not know how to help or what to do for you. If you live in a small community, you might not have support resources easily available to you.

"It takes a village to raise a child."

You might feel as though you will lose some of your privacy by sharing your personal health information with others. However, keeping your feelings to yourself can be stressful, and you might find it unburdening to share how you feel with someone outside your personal or family circle.

Expect that it will take you some time and effort to seek help and support throughout your breast cancer treatment.

❖ *What to do*

Throughout your treatment, you and your support partner will likely need help in several areas. For emotional and practical support, seek the cooperation of your close family and friends. Generally, friends and family want to help. Let them.

However, people often need direction on how they can help. Tell people how they can help and offer them specific jobs. You might consider creating a list of tasks and posting it in a central location. For example, you might ask people to help by driving your children to activities, cutting the grass, shoveling the driveway, shopping for groceries, or preparing meals that are easy to reheat. If you have a list ready when people call or visit, you can easily offer specific ways to help.

Get help parenting your children. You are not alone. Your family routines will change and people will have to take on new responsibilities. By allowing friends and family to be part of this difficult time in your life, you are telling them that they matter to you. However, try to keep new and different child caregivers to a minimum. It might be better to ask others to help with housework or yard work instead of providing childcare.

"You need to reach out to people for help. I eventually realized that reaching out to people wasn't a weakness, it was my greatest strength."

Ask supportive adults, such as teachers and neighbours, to monitor your children's behaviour, and to help by providing a caring presence or by encouraging your children to talk about your breast cancer. Ask other adults in your children's lives to keep in touch with you so that you can be aware of any issues that arise outside your home.

For medical support and information about other resources, you should speak with your health care team and contact the Canadian Cancer Society. You might also choose to investigate complementary healing therapies to help you through your treatment, although you need to discuss any treatments with your health care team before you start. For vital peer support and information, you should consider joining a breast cancer support group. For your emotional health, you might also consider speaking with a counselor. Your health care team can likely provide good information about counseling and other available resources. You might also seek support from your spiritual and cultural communities.

More often than not, if you ask, people are willing to help you.

Communicating with your Children

❧ What to expect

Stress is normal when a family is in crisis. When a parent is sick, it is difficult to keep family life normal. Children thrive on routine because it provides predictability and safety. You should expect to find a new normal or to change your old definition of normal for your family.

Your children might experience some stress and worry as you undergo treatment for your breast

"Everyone deals with stress differently."

cancer. When children experience stress, they can regress in their behaviour and ways of thinking. For example, a preschool-aged child might become clingy or begin bedwetting if you are admitted to the hospital or a teenager might test more limits than usual.

Your children might be bothered or embarrassed by other people's knowledge or perceptions of your breast cancer. For example, they might not know how to respond to questions from their friends and peers. Often, children do not want to be treated differently, whether positively or negatively, because of a parent's illness.

On the other hand, your children might be relieved if they are able to speak about your treatment with friends they trust.

If your physical appearance changes as a result of your treatment, such as if you lose your hair, or you are unable to participate in regular activities, such as carpooling or attending their sports events, your children might become embarrassed or uncomfortable. Again, children often do not want to be seen as different among their peer group. Remember that parents can be an embarrassment to children at times. Some children are not comfortable with the way that their parents look or act; for example, they can be too fat, too old, have the wrong hair colour, have an accent, or not dress the way that children consider suitable.

❧ What to do

Try to keep changes in your children's routine to a minimum. As much as possible, you should try to keep family rituals such as meal times, bed times, and birthdays on the same schedule. Try to maintain your children's participation in school and extracurricular activities and try

"I don't have all the answers. We're all learning as we go."

to attend school functions when you feel well enough.

If possible, try to schedule your treatment at convenient times when your children are in school or when your support partner, grandparent, friend, or daycare provider can care for your children.

Talk with your children throughout your treatment. Advise your children how changes in family routines will affect their lives. Help them understand the reality of the situation as best as you can. Let them know that you are still their parent and that you are still in charge. Tell them that you will get through the changes ahead together and that you will share information with them as soon as you know. Explain that you, yourself, do not know what to expect for the future, but that you can take it one day at a time, together.

Your children will benefit from knowing that your support partner is available and present to help you, and that you are not alone. If your children know that you have support from others, they will feel less worried about you and less likely to take on a caregiver role themselves.

Give your children information about your treatment that they can understand and give updates as you receive them. You might want to mark your treatment days on a family calendar to provide a visual reminder of when your energy levels might fluctuate. For example, you can mark the days that you receive treatment and the days that you should experience side effects. Tell your children the days that you might need and appreciate their help.

You might want to schedule a regular family meal or update session a few times a week so that you can share information about your health. A regularly scheduled meeting can provide your children with a sense of security if they know that you will share new information and that they will be able to ask questions. Update sessions are a good place to discuss how your breast cancer and treatment can change the family routine.

Give your children guidelines about what you consider public information about your treatment that they can discuss, and what you prefer to remain as private family information. If your children are not comfortable talking to friends about your breast cancer, or if they tell you they are being teased, tell them that they do not have to discuss it. They can bring it to you or your support partner to check out.

Try to remain physically and emotionally available to your children. Spend time together and pay attention to your children. Continue to plan time with your children. Try to set aside time to do fun things, such as take a short trip, look at family photos, or have a picnic. If your energy is low, try passive activities such as watching a movie, listening to music, or playing a board game. Conserve your energy and plan your day. Pace yourself so that you can do the things that are most important to you. Sometimes even watching a movie or listening to a conversation will require too much energy from you. Depending on the age and maturity of your children, their understanding of your energy and fatigue will vary. When your energy is low, tell your children how you feel and that you had hoped to finish the activity with them, but that you are too tired. Apologize and defer your plans, but try to spend time together at a later date. Even giving or asking your children for a hug can be comforting for them and for yourself. Even when you are feeling ill, you might be able to lie close to your children as you watch TV, watch a movie, or read together.

If your children can help you when you are not feeling well, encourage them to get involved, and praise their efforts when they do. There are many age-appropriate jobs that your children can do, such as setting the table, sweeping the floor, picking up toys, cleaning their rooms, and even cooking an occasional meal. If your children ask how they can help you, you could also suggest that they not argue or fight with their siblings. On days when you feel unwell, you can ask them to tell you a joke, read you a story, or draw you a picture. Even the youngest children can give you a hug or tell you about their day. Let your children know that any effort on their part can lift your spirits.

If you are likely to lose your hair from your treatment, you should let your children know in advance. Remember to tell your children that your hair loss is not permanent and that it will start to grow back after your treatment is finished. If your children are uncomfortable with your appearance during your treatment, you can reassure them that your appearance is a big change for you too. If they express discomfort with your appearance, you can ask your children what is bothering them and explain the reasons why you look that way in simple, clear words. Ask your children if they have suggestions or if they want to help you select a wig, hat, or scarf.

Questions and Answers

The following sample questions and answers can help you share treatment information with your children.

- **What kind of surgery do you need for breast cancer?**

  Breast cancer surgery may involve the removal of part of the breast (lumpectomy) or the whole breast (mastectomy). I may also have some glands removed from my armpit (lymph node disection). Any surgery causes pain and discomfort as the body recovers.

- **What is chemotherapy and how does it work?**

  Chemotherapy is the process of using medicine to destroy cancer cells. Sometimes a doctor uses chemotherapy to improve the chances for a cure. Cancer cells grow fast, as do some of our healthy cells, such as the cells in our hair, mouth, and stomach. Chemotherapy kills cancer cells, but sometimes it also affects healthy cells. This fact explains why people receiving chemotherapy can lose their hair, have a sore mouth, upset stomach, and feel very tired. The medicine cannot tell the difference between the cancer cells and the healthy cells. The good part is that our healthy cells can repair themselves after chemotherapy, but cancer cells usually cannot.

- **How do you receive chemotherapy?**

  You can receive chemotherapy in several ways. Some of the medicines are pills that you swallow with water and others are medicines that doctors or nurses put directly into your veins through a needle and tube in your arm.

- **How long does chemotherapy take?**

  Chemotherapy is different for each person, and varies according to that person's situation. On average, people receive chemotherapy every three weeks for four to six months before all the treatment is finished.

- **Why do people lose their hair during chemotherapy?**

  Not all chemotherapy drugs cause hair loss. Of the drugs that do, not everyone loses their hair. The medicine can kill the fast-growing hair cells, because it cannot tell the difference between the hair cells that grow quickly and the cancer cells that grow quickly. Hair starts to grow back after chemotherapy is finished. Sometimes the new hair can be a different colour or be curlier than it was before.

- **Why are people tired during chemotherapy?**

  Chemotherapy drugs are powerful chemicals that can make people feel very tired. Often this is caused by having fewer red blood cells which provide energy to the body. Feeling tired after receiving chemotherapy can last for a few days or even longer.

- **Why should you not be around people with colds or go to crowded places?**

  Chemotherapy also affects healthy white blood cells, which help fight infections. When you have fewer white blood cells, it is harder to fight germs, so it is better to avoid getting too close to other people who might spread germs.

- **Why does chemotherapy make a person feel sick?**

  Chemotherapy can also affect the healthy cells inside our stomachs, which grow quickly. When people receive chemotherapy, they can feel nauseous and throw up. There are medicines called anti-emetics that can help you feel less sick to your stomach.

- **What is radiation therapy?**

  Radiation is a treatment that destroys cancer cells in the body. Radiation therapy (or external beam radiation) uses a machine that directs highenergy rays at the part of the body that needs treatment. These x-rays are much more powerful than the ones that check if you have broken bones or cavities in your teeth.

- **How do you receive radiation therapy?**

  To receive radiation therapy, I have to lie on a table in a room where I will be alone while the treatment is given. The radiation therapist can see me through a window and I can talk to the therapist through a speaker. Treatment lasts for a few minutes at a time and will be done each weekday for a few weeks. Radiation only treats one part of the body at a time; it does not go through the whole body.

- **Does radiation therapy make you sick or lose your hair?**

  Your reaction to radiation therapy depends on what part of your body you receive the radiation. Because you only receive radiation in one part of your body, the results are different for everybody. I will lose my hair if I have radiation on my head. Usually, you feel sick only if you have radiation in the stomach area. Radiation treatment can make you feel very tired during treatment and for weeks or months afterward. Sometimes, the area that is treated can be sore and look like a sunburn.

Treatment

- **Can I see a radiation therapy machine?**

  I can check with the radiation therapy staff to see if you can come to one of my visits. They will probably let you see the machine before I have treatment. You cannot go in the room while the radiation machine is on.

- **Why does your arm swell after you receive treatment?**

  Our bodies have many systems in them and each system has a job to do. For example, the digestive system breaks down the food that we eat and brings nourishment to all of our cells, and the nervous system sends impulses to our muscles to make them move. The lymphatic system has many functions, and one of them is to remove fluid from between our cells and the waste products that our cells produce. These waste products and fluids travel through a series of very thin tubes, called vessels, and bean-shaped bumps, called nodes. When the doctors remove the cancer, they have to also take out some of the lymph nodes to make sure that the cancer is not in them. Without these lymph nodes, the lymphatic system sometimes does not work as well, and fluid can get trapped in the tissues in the arm and cannot get out.

- **What is lymphedema?**

  Lymphedema occurs when the lymphatic system cannot drain the fluid from between cells. If the vessels of the lymphatic system are blocked, or if the nodes are removed or not working, the fluid builds up and causes swelling. In other words, lymphedema is a chronic swelling from fluid not being able to drain from the lymph system. You can get lymphedema if your lymph nodes are removed or if you have radiation treatment for breast cancer. Not everyone gets lymphedema.

- **Does lymphedema go away?**

  The swelling might not go away completely, but there are gentle treatments and special bandages that I can wear to keep it from getting any worse and reduce the swelling.

- **Can I catch lymphedema from you?**

  No, the swelling comes from the operation that I had. The swelling is not like being sick, so you cannot catch it.

- **Do all women with breast cancer get lymphedema?**

  No, sometimes the doctors only have to take one or two nodes, or sometimes the arm already has other lymphatic pathways in place so that the fluid does not get stuck in it. Sometimes the arm only gets swollen after it gets a cut or mosquito bite, or an injury, and then the lymphatic system gets overwhelmed.

Treatment

Common concerns	• Family life is disrupted by treatment demands and its side effects • Work is interrupted and finances might be reduced • Emotional and physical needs are high
Parent with cancer	• Treatment effects: nausea, fatigue, anxiety • Body image: surgery, breast changes, weight changes • Reduced capacity to parent and increased demands on support partners
Support partner	• Increased responsibility for caring for ill parent as well as for children and household • Fatigue and feelings of being overwhelmed, yet might not receive support from family, friends, or from the workplace
Children	• Parents might not be as available as before • Need for attention from their ill parent, as well as other caring adults • Need for family life and routines to continue
Coping tips	• Maintain family life as much as possible but be flexible and realistic • Spell out concrete examples how your illness and treatment will affect your children's daily lives • Give children age-appropriate tasks to encourage their participation • Tap into your children's ability to help and comfort you without overloading them or making them caregivers • Let others help • Take it one day at a time • Keep alternate care givers to a minimum • Seek a variety of resources such as support groups, spirituality/cultural community, complementary therapies, books, and library resources

Financial Concerns

Financial Concerns

Taking Care of Yourself

❊ What to expect

Whether you work outside the home or are a stay-at-home parent, breast cancer might affect your ability to work, which can change your financial situation. If you work outside the home, you might have to leave your job either temporarily or permanently. If you work at home, you might face additional costs for childcare if you are unable to provide it. It is normal to worry about money and how to provide for your family if you are not able to work as before.

When you have breast cancer, you might have to deal with the following financial realities:

- You might have to make changes in your family's lifestyle.

- You might have less disposable income.

- You might have to use your savings.

- Your plans for the future might change.

A decrease in your income can also have an emotional and social impact on you and your family. You might worry about how you are going to manage personally if you are separated from your job and from your friends at work. If work is important in your life as a source of satisfaction, meaning, and enjoyment, an inability to work can affect you even more.

"How will I pay my bills?"

Some of the additional costs of receiving treatment can include:

- Some prescription medications you take at home such as drugs to treat side effects of treatment (nausea, diarrhea, fatigue, infections, etc.)
- Other types of treatments for side effects (such as physiotherapy for lymphedema, massage therapy)
- Transportation and/or parking costs
- Additional child or family care costs
- Extra meal costs
- Additional home help
- Special requirements (such as wigs, prosthesis, lymphedema supplies)

All of these concerns are normal and often resources are available to help you cope.

What to do

It is important for you to understand and manage your personal finances. You should review and compare the money that you have coming in, and your financial commitments. A review such as this can help you decide what changes you need to make. To feel more in control of your finances, draw up a detailed budget and examine carefully what expenses are important and make any adjustments that you can.

To start, you should review the following financial items:

- Monthly expenses
- Assets, both property and savings
- Debts
- Mortgage, and whether it provides disability or life insurance

"Take charge of your own finances."

- Credit cards
- Car payments
- Insurance policies, and what they cover

When you are not working, try to make an effort to stay connected. Reach out, and schedule get-togethers with your friends, if your health allows. Staying informed about what is happening with people, both personally and professionally, can help you remain connected.

Getting Support

❊ What to expect

While you have breast cancer, there are several programs that can help you financially. Government programs, insurance policies, and community organizations are often available to provide services or subsidies. Because programs and services vary across Canada and even from municipality to municipality, you need to learn what kind of financial assistance is offered in your particular area.

When you are ill, you might lack the energy or feel too overwhelmed to find out about sources of income to which you are entitled. Applying for benefits can be both physically and emotionally demanding. If you have been independent, or if you are a private person, it might be difficult to ask for help. If you have no source of income, applying for social assistance may cause you embarassment or shame. Remember that these programs exist there to help people in time of need. While you are ill, it is important to use all the resources that are available.

"Making applications can be exhausting. It requires energy and a clear mind."

If you are investigating how to obtain financial support, you should consider the following things:

- Your eligibility for support
- Application procedures
- Required forms and documentation, such as a doctor's certificate
- Fees
- Delayed waiting periods

❖ *What to do*

Ensure that you are well informed about your personal financial options as well as any government-sponsored income replacement programs. For information on financial assistance and other community resources, a social worker at your local hospital or Cancer Centre may be able to assist you. Ask your support partner, or friend to help you make any necessary applications.

Financial Resources

You should be aware of the following resources that might help replace or supplement your income while you recover from breast cancer:

Provincial governments and municipalities

Programs for social assistance and disability support are available to help persons in need when they cannot work. Eligibility for benefits depends on your family income level and on the value of your other assets.

Personnel department at your workplace

If you have been working outside the home, your human resources (HR) or personnel department at your workplace is a good place to start. If you

"Everyone should take advantage of the resources in the community that are available to help them."

work full-time and have benefits, there might be a significant time for which you can be absent from work and still be paid. Your HR department can give you details on the following benefits:

- Sick leave
- Vacation entitlement
- Short and long-term disability
- Leave of absence, without pay
- Early retirement options

Unions

If you are a member of a union, your union can help you understand the details about workplace programs and group benefits for obtaining paid or unpaid leaves of absence, extended health care benefits, and life insurance. If there is a dispute with your employer about your eligibility for programs, consult the union about your rights.

Private health insurance policies

If you have a private health insurance policy, it might offer coverage for sickness and disability.

Service Canada

This government department offers programs for which you or your caregivers might be eligible:

- **Employment Insurance Sickness Benefits (EI)**

  With these benefits, you can receive payment for sickness benefits for a maximum of 15 weeks. To be eligible for this benefit, you must have 600 hours of insurable employment in the last 52 weeks or since the start of your last EI claim. Some exceptions are allowed. There is a two-week waiting period before you receive any benefits. However, if you receive paid sick leave from your employer or group insurance benefits you might not have to wait the two weeks to receive some income.

- **Compassionate Care Benefit Program**

  This program allows members of a family to have a total of six weeks of benefits to care for a dying relative. More than one caregiver can claim the benefit, but the time allowed is related to the person who is ill.

- **Canada Pension Plan (CPP) or Quebec Pension Plan (QPP) Disability Benefits**
  (QPP is administered through La Régie des rentes du Québec)

  You qualify for these benefits based on a medical need and not on financial need. To be eligible, your illness must be prolonged and severe, you must have enough CPP contributions, and you must be between the ages of 18 and 65. These disability benefits are deducted from your private disability insurance and are taxable. The benefits start four months after you are deemed to have become disabled. Dependent children might be eligible for benefits if they are under 18 or are between the ages of 18 and 25, and if they attend school full time.

  CPP and QPP also provide death benefits and survivor benefits.

- **Canada/Quebec Pension Plan Retirement Benefits**

  You can receive these retirement benefits as early as age 60, but they are reduced by 0.5 % for each month the person who retires is younger than age 65.

Life insurance

Some life insurance policies allow owners to access funds before death. However, you should carefully weigh the advantages and disadvantages of prematurely accessing any funds.

Disability tax credit

The disability tax credit can be applied for through the Taxation Office of the Canada Revenue

Agency, using Form T2201. This tax credit is non-refundable and reduces the amount of federal income tax that you pay. You are eligible to apply if you have "a severe and prolonged (at least 12 months) mental or physical impairment such that you are markedly restricted in your ability to perform a basic activity of daily living."

Financial advisors

A financial advisor can help you determine sources in your assets from which you can raise money without necessarily depleting your cash or other savings such as registered retirement savings plans (RRSPs). For example, you might take out a mortgage on property that you own, or use an asset to secure a line of credit. You can find financial advisors at your bank, trust company, or credit union, or at a community organization that offers financial planning services, or you might have a friend or acquaintance with professional financial planning expertise.

Other Possible Expenses and Resources

Transportation

Every centre/hospital has different levels of support available to help with transportation costs. Talk to a member of your care team to find out what is available at your centre.

Credit and budget counseling

These counseling options might be useful if your debts are already significant. These services are often available through not-for-profit community service agencies and they aim to help you consolidate your debts and develop a budget to match your means.

Prescription drugs

Drugs given in your Cancer Centre or in hospital are usually covered by provincial health plans.

Drugs that you take at home may be covered in whole or in part by your extended health insurance plans from work or private insurance.

For the following people, some provincial health care programs cover most prescription medications:

- Recipients of social assistance or provincial disability support programs
- Recipients of medical or nursing help at home, through a provincial health plan
- Senior citizens
- Persons whose prescription costs exceed a certain amount

Your provincial health care program might have a co-payment or a deductible amount. Some pharmacies might waive the co-payment fee if you ask.

Home support services

Support services such as nursing or personal support assistance might be available to you as part of your provincial health plan. These services are usually requested by your treating physician.

Medical equipment and supplies

Some medical equipment, such as prostheses or wheelchairs might be covered or subsidized as part of your provincial health care benefits or through a municipal program if you are a lowincome earner. These supplies might also be covered through private or workplace extended health insurance plans if you have a doctor's authorization.

Wigs

Check with your private insurance company to see if they will cover the costs of a wig. If you receive social assistance, the cost may be covered. You might require a medical prescription to receive reimbursement.

If the costs are not covered by an insurance program, ask a member your health care team for information on possible sources or assistance in purchasing a wig. The local chapters of the Canadian Cancer Society are sometimes able to provide donated wigs at no cost to you.

Cancer support organizations

Support organizations can provide helpful services such as support groups, exercise programs, and transportation to and from medical appointments. Contact the Canadian Cancer Society or other cancer support programs in your area.

Childcare

Childcare and other children's needs might be subsidized for low-income earners or for people who receive social assistance or provincial disability support. Some day care providers also have a sliding fee scale.

Housing

If your income is reduced you may be eligible for housing where the rent is based on your income.

Bank, trust company, or credit union

Ask if your mortgage or other debts or lines of credit contain a disability clause. Your regular monthly payments might be covered for you or you might be able to put them on hold or cancel them during times of illness. You might also be able to renegotiate loans.

Communicating with your Children

❧ What to expect

Children might worry that having a parent with breast cancer will affect the family financially.

Your children might ask the following questions if your family finances are reduced:

- Will I still get an allowance?
- Will I have to stop my after school activities?
- Will we be able to afford my tuition for college, private school, or university?
- Will we have to move?
- Will I have to get a job to contribute to the family finances?

Children will react differently to changes in financial circumstances. It is normal for them to be co-operative, angry or resentful. They can have all of these reactions at different times.

❧ What to do

You need to address their concerns and involve them as much as is reasonable for their age. Be clear about what the changes are, and how long you expect these changes to last.

It is your responsibility as a parent to support your children financially. However depending on their level of maturity, enlist their co-operation and involvement in making decisions that affect them. Have them make a list of what things they believe are necessary and what they can do without.

"Can I still play hockey?"

For younger children, find ways for them to contribute, such as having a smaller allowance, which may help them feel part of the process.

School-aged children have the ability to understand about finances. Older children can participate in different ways, such as taking on a part-time job to pay for their own spending money.

Regardless of their age, your children can contribute ideas to help your family manage with less money. This participation gives them the chance to understand and help solve the problem. Your children are more likely to co-operate and accept financial changes if they are involved in an appropriate way in the decision-making.

Find ways to let your children know their contribution is helping, such as saying thank you regularly.

If your children become angry or resentful, it is important to remember that their frustration over financial matters is also frustration with the whole situation, and you may need to address their concerns on those different levels.

"What else can you do but tell kids the truth?"

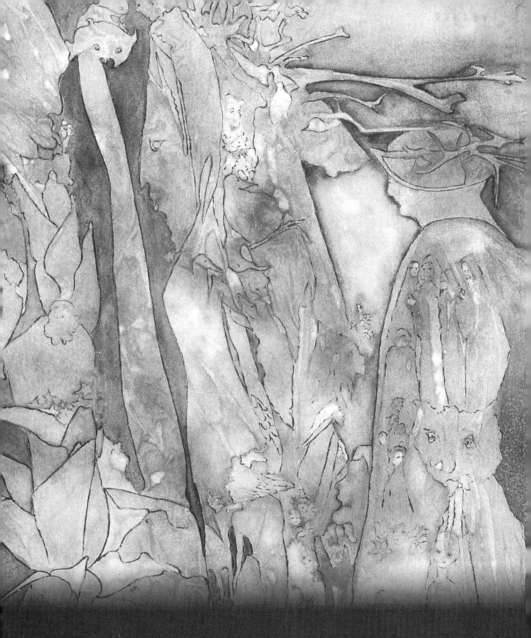

Survivorship

Survivorship

Taking Care of Yourself

✤ What to expect

People often look forward to the end of cancer treatment, so that their lives can return to a more normal lifestyle. The period of time after treatment is typically called survivorship. During survivorship, expectations and reality often collide.

Survivorship is different for each person. It can be a very long period of time, to which you adjust easily, or a time when you face many challenges and potential setbacks in your health. Survivorship can be many things, including a time of acceptance, a time of adjustment, and a time of progress. Regardless of the kind of treatment you received, it will have affected you. After treatment, it is normal to be physically and emotionally exhausted.

Going through treatment for cancer can be compared to running a race. When runners finish a race, they slow down, stop running, and take time to recover. Long-distance runners might stop entirely and collapse on the ground at the finish line. Similarly, people who are recovering from breast cancer treatment might need time to let their bodies adjust.

Physically, you are not the same person who started treatment a few months before. You might have had surgery, chemotherapy, radiation, or a combination of treatments. After any treatment, you are likely to have less energy than you did

"Treatment was a like a roller coaster ride. It was a long ride and eventually I returned, but to a new, unfamiliar place."

before. Gradually, your energy should return, but it might take longer than you expect. Surgery or radiation changes your body, and might leave a permanent imprint. Any changes to your body can affect your body image, which, in turn, can affect your sexual relationship.

Emotionally, you might feel vulnerable after your treatment ends. Likely, your experience of being diagnosed and treated for breast cancer affected your views on life, mortality, and who and what is important to you. It is not unusual for your outlook and priorities to change because of your cancer experience. You might feel sad or anxious about your health or your family. You might wonder if the cancer is gone or if it will return. After treatment, you might experience mixed emotions. You might miss the familiarity of a medical routine and the regular contact with your health care team. You might feel hope, gratitude, and relief to have finished treatment, but you might also feel apprehensive, cautious, and uncertain about the future.

Dealing with the physical and emotional adjustments after treatment can take a lot of energy. You might feel disappointed or frustrated if you cannot meet your own physical or emotional expectations, or those of your family. You might feel isolated and as though you do not belong. You might want to withdraw from the people who are closest to you.

After treatment, you might regain your energy and return to a normal routine quite quickly and feel as though your breast cancer is behind you. Or, you might have more difficulty moving past the experiences of diagnosis and treatment. Regardless, breast cancer has affected your life. Your life can return to normal after treatment, but it might be a new normal that needs time to evolve.

❧ *What to do*

Your mindset is an important aspect of your breast cancer survivorship. A positive outlook can greatly influence your experience. Life is never static. The experience of living with cancer can teach you new things about yourself, your friends and your family. Breast cancer gives your family the unwanted opportunity to accept hardship, to adjust, and to move forward. People often claim that cancer makes them appreciate things that they previously took for granted. Your experience can give you and the people around you the opportunity to grow, to be strong in the face of adversity, and to realize life's potential.

Try to dwell on the positives. Life after treatment can be very good. You probably have a new perspective on life and a new appreciation of the pleasures, both large and small, that life can hold. Give yourself time to get back into a regular routine and be open to making changes as necessary. A positive attitude and flexible nature might be one of the best gifts that you can give your children, as it will teach them how to deal with change, an integral part of life, in a healthy way.

Take time to recover from your treatment. Make it a priority to take care of your physical and mental health. Listen to your body. Be aware that fatigue is normal and often temporary. Pay attention to what you are capable of and which activities are too much for you. Set your own pace and plan for a gradual return to your former responsibilities. You might need a less busy agenda at home and at work. Pay attention to your own expectations and evaluate whether they are realistic. Adjust your expectations about what you can do now and what you will be able to do in the future. Take your recovery one step at a time. Be clear in your communications. Talk with your support partner, family, and friends

"Let the new normal evolve."

about how much of your responsibilities you are able to resume and at what rate. Your expectations of yourself might be quite different from theirs.

Take time to pamper and be good to yourself. Try to incorporate activities and things that give you pleasure, such as taking walks, taking baths, listening to your favourite music, reading, or watching movies.

Explore some activities to take care of yourself such as: join a support group; enjoy the benefits of massage therapy; focus on your physical well being and fitness by joining a gym. Seek out a nutritionist to improve your diet and eating habits. If you have difficulty getting started, or feel depressed, speak to the social worker in your health care team.

Work with the people around you to make a new normal that works for everyone.

Getting Support

❖ What to expect

Because you might look better, the people around you might not recognize the adjustment and recovery time that you need to heal and regain your energy. Those close to you might expect you to return to normal before you are ready. Your friends and family might have difficulty understanding that you need time to recover and you might have a hard time avoiding the pressure to return to a regular routine as soon as possible. Your friends and family might also not understand your feelings and emotions and might be distressed to see you distracted, tired, or worried at a time when they expect you to be healthy again.

"Tomorrow is a new day."

"Make emotional connections."

Specifically, support partners can also experience mixed emotions as your treatment ends. Support partners are usually relieved, optimistic, and hopeful for successful treatment results, but might expect you to recuperate quickly. Your support partner might need to provide care and support to you and your children for longer than you expected. Survivorship can be a challenging time for everyone, when expectations and feelings need to be re-evaluated and balanced.

❊ What to do

If you have not done so already, survivorship can be a good time to seek out peer support.

Linking with other cancer survivors can be beneficial and sharing your feelings and experiences with others who are experiencing the same thing can be helpful and relieving. Now that you have finished treatment, you might have more time to attend support group meetings and might have had more time to reflect on what you have experienced. Remember that each person's medical situation is unique, but that you often share similar concerns with others.

You should take time to discuss with your support partner and family what you are and are not capable of. The most helpful thing you can do for the people around you is to keep them informed of what is happening to you, how you are feeling, and what they can do to help. Try your best to keep others aware of the support that you need. Ask your support network, including friends, family, and teachers, for their continued assistance.

Survivorship

Communicating with your Children

✦ What to expect

Your children's reaction to the end of your treatment will vary according to their ages. Younger children will not understand your physical and emotional limits, and will expect care and attention as usual. They will not understand that the end of your treatment is not the same thing as being completely recovered. Because of what they have experienced themselves, most young children understand any illness to involve a brief period of sickness and a rapid recovery.

Older children are better able to appreciate that your recovery might take more time and that some things will not be the same as before your diagnosis and treatment. However, older children might feel resentful if they have to continue the additional tasks and responsibilities that they accepted during your treatment.

Your children might be angry, frustrated, or confused if events have not happened as they expected. Your children might feel as though things are worse if your treatment has not restored you to perfect health immediately. On the other hand, your children might think that you look exactly as you did before your treatment.

✦ What to do

During survivorship, as before, it is important to be honest with your children so that they can make sense of the changes that are happening around them. If you talk about what is happening to you and how it affects them, you can show

"You look okay, so you must be okay."

"I might look like my old self and sometimes I might even act like I used to, but there are days when I don't feel good and often I don't have the energy I used to have to do all the things I want to do."

Survivorship

your children that they are important to you and can help instill a sense of security.

Continue to give your children age-appropriate information on how you are feeling and how your survivorship affects their lives. Let them know what you are and are not capable of. Explain that you will still need to make adjustments to your family life and your routines, even after your treatment has finished. Engage your children in discussion. Clarify your children's expectations about the end of your treatment, and encourage them to talk about their feelings.

Survivorship

Common concerns	• Time of complex emotions
	• Expectations and reality often collide
	• Stress of survivorship can be both physical and emotional
	• Fear of recurrence
Parent with cancer	• Fewer medical appointments can be relieving, but might reduce some of your support resources
	• Family and friends might reduce their support if they think you are back to normal
	• Sense of failure if you think that you should feel normal but you don't
	• You look better but you're not
	• Pressure to return to daily routines and work
	• Still wanting to protect your family
Support partner	• Partner looks better but is not feeling better
	• Desire to help partner return to normal
	• Desire for partner to return to work to ease financial pressure
Children	• Information and help to understand the opposing message that their parent looks better, but is not the same as before
	• Need for family life and routines to continue
	• Knowledge of their parents feelings and how your reduced energy affects them
	• Attention to and reassurance of their feelings, thoughts and expectations

Coping tips	• Take time to find your new self and share your true self with loved ones
	• Develop a new definition for what is normal
	• Take time before rushing back to work
	• Learn to manage fear of recurrence through complementary therapies and support groups
	• Do not project your fear of recurrence onto others, especially your children
	• Be patient, forgiving, and nurturing to yourself

Survivorship

Heredity and Genetic Testing

Heredity and Genetic Testing

Taking Care of Yourself

❖ What to expect

After you are diagnosed with breast cancer, you might fear or worry that your children will develop breast cancer because of the genetic link that you share.

As a parent, it is natural for you to be concerned for your children, and the possibility of carrying or passing on the genetic predisposition for breast cancer can make you feel guilt and fear for yourself, your support partner, and your children.

The reality is that most breast cancer is not hereditary. In fact, current research shows that only 5-10% of breast cancer is caused by a mutation in a gene that can be inherited. A gene is the basic unit of heredity. As humans, we have thousands of genes that instruct and guide how our bodies grow and develop. A mutation is anything that causes a gene to differ from its natural state. A mutation might cause a disease, or it might cause a harmless variation to a gene.

Genetic testing, through a blood test, might be able to determine whether a person carries a mutation in a gene that is associated with an increased risk of developing breast or ovarian cancer. The same gene mutation that causes a predisposition to hereditary breast cancer also increases the risk of developing ovarian cancer.

"After I learned that I had breast cancer, I worried about whether I had passed it on to my kids."

59

Genetic testing can determine who else in your family might have an increased risk of developing cancer so that they can inform their doctors and receive more informed medical attention. Genetic testing can also provide relief to family members who learn that their risk for developing cancer is the same as anyone else in the general population.

The risk of inheriting breast cancer also applies to males. Sons and daughters can both inherit the gene mutations that increase the risk for breast cancer and can pass them on to their own children. Less than 1% of breast cancer occurs in males in the general population, but this risk can be higher for men in families where there is an inherited form of breast cancer. There is also an increased risk of prostate cancer for men in such families.

An inherited form of breast cancer might be present in your family if several blood relatives, from at least two different generations, have had breast or ovarian cancer and meet any of the following conditions:

- You were diagnosed before age 50

- You were diagnosed with bilateral breast cancer

- You were diagnosed with both breast and ovarian cancer

- You have a male relative diagnosed with breast cancer

Giving a blood sample for genetic testing might seem like a simple and practical issue, but it can be an emotionally charged decision for you and your family. Your decision to be tested also affects your blood relatives and extended family such as parents, aunts, uncles, cousins, siblings, and your children.

There are limits to what genetic testing can achieve, and it will not resolve all of your or your family's concerns.

Some people find it relatively easy to decide whether to pursue genetic testing, but find it difficult when they receive the test results, especially if the results indicate that a gene mutation is present. If you test positive for the cancer-predisposing gene, you must decide how, when, and with whom to share the information.

❋ What to do

Do not wait for your doctor to introduce the possibility of genetic testing. You should raise the issue yourself.

Not everyone who enquires about genetics testing will receive it. Discuss your family history with your doctor and ask if a referral for genetic counseling and testing is appropriate. If your family meets some of the characteristics of a genetic pre-disposition for breast cancer, a referral will be made.

As you think about your feelings about genetic testing, you should remember several important facts:

- It is not your fault that you have breast cancer.

- You cannot change the genes that you were born with.

- Your breast cancer does not define who you are as a person or as a parent.

As you make any decisions about genetic testing, do whatever you need to do to cope with your feelings of guilt, anger, and fear for yourself, your children and family members.

"There is no right answer when it comes to genetic testing."

Your decision about whether to pursue genetic testing is a highly personal one. Genetic testing is a complex issue that requires you and those who are close to you to be well informed about the advantages and disadvantages of genetic testing.

As you think about genetic testing, you should consider these positive and negative aspects:

Positive aspects of obtaining genetic testing

- Testing can show whether or not you have an altered gene that your children or other relatives might inherit.

- Testing might help you reduce your risk of future cancer through early medical intervention.

- Testing can help you alert your children or other relatives and their doctors to the need for extra monitoring for breast or ovarian cancer so that it can be detected as early as possible.

Negative aspects of obtaining genetic testing

- A negative genetic test result does not absolutely guarantee that a genetic mutation is not present.

- If the test results do not detect that you have the cancer gene mutation, you might have a false sense of security about whether those around you could develop cancer.

- Sharing positive test results with children and other family members can be difficult.

- Other family members may not agree with your decision to be tested, which may cause problems within your family. Genetic counselors may help you work through these issues.

- Positive results might lead to greater worry about cancer risk for yourself and your children.

- As with any part of your medical file, test results might not remain private.

- Positive results might impact policies for health insurance or life insurance.

Positive aspects of declining genetic testing

- You can avoid a positive test result and the burden on you or your children of knowing about an increased risk of cancer.

- You will not have any documentation of a pre-existing condition that could affect insurance policies.

Negative aspects of declining genetic testing

- You will not know whether the cause of your cancer was hereditary.

- You will not know whether your family is at high risk for developing cancer.

- You might not be able to participate in some of the medical surveillance programs for people at high risk of developing cancer.

Getting Support

❊ *What to expect*

In Canada, genetic testing is performed through the genetics departments of certain hospitals. Your doctor will know where the nearest clinic is located. Before you and your health care team make any decision about having genetic testing, you will have an appointment with a genetic counselor. Genetic testing in Canada is always done within the context of genetic counseling. Genetic counseling can help you determine whether you are a candidate for genetic testing and can also help clarify the advantages and disadvantages of testing.

Genetic counselors offer you their support based on their expertise in this area. Social workers, nurses, and psychologists at your local Cancer Centre or community health centre might also

"Cancer was certainly not in my plan for my family."

be available to you as you manage your decisions about or reactions to genetic testing.

When genetic testing is offered to a family that is suspected of carrying a gene mutation, the genetic testing is performed first on the family member with a diagnosis of breast cancer.

❖ What to do

Ask your doctor about your eligibility for genetic testing. If your doctor refers you to a genetic counselor, discuss the implications of genetic testing, and think about yourself, as well as your support partner, siblings, extended family members, and your children.

If your family is an appropriate candidate for genetic testing, you still have the choice of whether or not to complete the testing. Whether you take the test is ultimately your decision. Weigh all of the information that you have, and make the best decision based on your circumstances.

Communicating with your Children

❖ What to expect

Some children, particularly adolescent and young adult daughters might believe that they will develop breast cancer. Your children might speak openly about their concerns or they might keep their feelings to themselves.

If you receive genetic testing, sharing the results with your children but also with your other family members can be difficult. How much information you share, and when you share it, is an individual choice.

"Every situation is different."

"If you have breast cancer, will I get it too?"

64

If you test positive for a cancer-predisposing gene mutation, you might be anxious for your relatives and children to undergo genetic testing to determine whether they have inherited the gene or whether they require extra medical monitoring for the development of breast or ovarian cancer. However, it is not your decision whether they receive genetic testing. After your children reach the age of majority, they must decide whether or not to undergo testing. As it was for you, the decision to receive genetic testing is an individual choice.

❧ *What to do*

If you test positive for carrying the gene mutation for breast cancer, you might prefer to delay sharing the test results until your children are 18, when they can be tested for the cancer-predisposing gene.

You might want to avoid causing your children to worry about their genetic makeup, at least until they are old enough to do something to relieve their worry or until they can be routinely checked medically.

However, certain circumstances might make you want to tell your children earlier. If your children know that you had genetic testing, they might expect to hear the results, and might be apprehensive or misunderstand if you do not share the results. Your children might think that silence implies bad news, and would benefit from hearing about the results.

You might also want to tell your children if the results affect you emotionally. Your children will be aware that something is wrong and might reach the wrong conclusions about why. If you plan any preventative surgery (such as mastectomy or removal of ovaries), your children might need

"You can't always protect your kids, even though you want to."

to understand why, which is a good opportunity to explain your genetic test results.

If you discuss genetic testing with your children, you should offer age-appropriate information and answer their questions as best as you can. It is better for children to have accurate information than to live with wrong assumptions or unspoken fears. If you withhold information, older children might feel as though you are excluding them from important family matters. Your children might resent, for example, learning about your test results from someone else instead of from you or having to wait until they are 18 before they are informed. If you choose to wait to tell your children about your test results, you should explain to them your reasoning, perhaps in a letter that accompanies the test results. This letter can be shared with them when they are older.

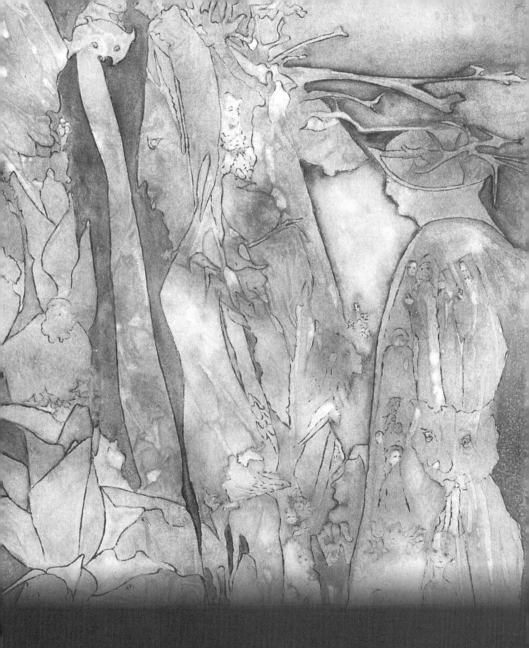

Recurrence or Metastases

Recurrence or Metastases

Taking Care of Yourself

✣ What to expect

Some, but not all, people experience a recurrence of breast cancer, which can happen years after their initial diagnosis.

A recurrence of breast cancer does not necessarily mean that the cancer has spread to other parts of the body. A recurrence can be limited to the breast, and it might happen more than once. A recurrence can be treated in several ways, including surgery, radiation, chemotherapy, and hormonal treatments. Often, local recurrences can be cured.

Metastases means that the cancer has spread to another part of the body. Often, cancer spreads to the bone, chest wall, lungs, liver, or brain. Metastases is a chronic disease that cannot be cured, but it can usually be controlled for some period of time with treatment. For some people, the initial diagnosis of cancer starts with metastases.

It is important to know that even if your cancer spreads or metastasizes, in most cases it does not mean that death is near. Many people receive treatment for metastatic cancer that enables them to live with cancer for increasing periods of time. For some women, however, metastases can be immediately life-threatening. If this is the case,

"It's back."

69

your doctor will discuss the seriousness of the situation with you.

Hearing from your doctor that your breast cancer has recurred or that it has spread, or metastasized, is often as devastating a shock as the original diagnosis. As with your initial diagnosis, you will need time to understand and adjust to the news.

A breast cancer recurrence usually means that you will need to receive more treatment. You should discuss the variety of available treatment options with your doctor. If one treatment becomes less effective, you might need another treatment regimen. Your doctor might even suggest that you participate in a clinical trial of new treatments.

Your experience with a recurrence of breast cancer or with metastases might be brief or it might continue for years.

❧ *What to do*

As with your initial diagnosis, it is important that you take good care of yourself first.

Educate yourself about your medical situation so that you understand what is happening to your body and understand clearly the goals of your treatment. For example, you should understand whether your proposed treatment is meant to cure or to control your cancer. Inform yourself about your treatment options and take an active role in your treatment and medical decisions.

Living with a chronic illness has implications for you as well as for your support partner and children. Adapting to changes in your health while your family is growing poses special challenges for everyone over a period of time. There is no right or wrong way to manage a chronic illness. There is no easy answer for how best to adapt. Some of the best advice that you can take is to

"I'll do whatever it takes."

live each day as best as you can. Do not let your cancer control all of your life or your family's life. Remember that life continues and that it does not always revolve around your breast cancer.

More than anything, you should remain hopeful. Your new challenge is to live life as fully as possible, even if your illness recurs or advances, and to maintain routine and order for yourself and your family. Fortunately, more and more people are living longer with metastases. Many people undergo treatment and their disease often remains stable for long periods of time. Some people find that they can return to work and maintain a family routine.

Getting Support

✤ **What to expect**

If your breast cancer recurs or you develop metastases, you will likely return to some form of treatment and will have reduced energy. Under ideal circumstances, your support partner will play a greater role with your children and provide care for you. Realistically, your support partner alone might not be able to do all that is required or sustain the level of required care over time.

The people who are close to you might have different reactions to the recurrence or metastases of your breast cancer. Crises can sometimes exaggerate existing family relationships. Some people might easily support you again and be helpful and others might withdraw because they are afraid or because they are overwhelmed. These reactions are natural and might subside over time.

"Hope for the best and prepare for the worst."

If you are diagnosed with metastases, you might think more about death and dying, even if death is not imminent. You might find it a relief to settle some legal affairs such as your will, guardianship for your children, and power of attorney. Many parents feel uncomfortable about these decisions, but making them often reduces worry and anxiety.

Without these documents, no one else truly knows what you want. During the process of settling these legal affairs, you might encounter resistance from people who are close to you. These are normal and common reactions because it is upsetting to think about what would happen if you died.

❖ *What to do*

As with your initial diagnosis, it is important for you to set up a structured support team. You are not alone. Your recurrence or metastases affects both you and those close to you. As much as possible, keep the lines of communication open with those around you. Continue to talk about what is happening to you, the effects that it has, and the support that you need.

Depend on your support partner and those close to you to help lighten your parenting role. As you receive treatment, you will again have reduced energy. If you are overwhelmed, seek and accept help from family, friends and neighbours, as well as through Cancer Centre support resources. Make decisions with your support partner about who to ask and when you need help. If you rely on others, you can conserve precious energy and free more time to rest and to spend with family. Encourage the support of grandparents, extended family, and friends. If you do not have support people readily available, seek out other support networks for help. Your health care team can also help you find other resources that are available in

"There is no such thing as too early."

your community. If you are unsure where to get help, the following resources can get you started:

- Your health care team
- Your Cancer Centre library
- Your local chapter of the Canadian Cancer Society
- Cancer support groups, particularly those that are devoted to people living with metastases

If you have the energy and interest to settle legal or administrative decisions, discuss them with your support partner and do it. Legally recording your personal wishes is the only way to ensure that others know and carry out exactly what you want. After you make these decisions, you can stop thinking or worrying about them and proceed with living your life. You might ask your support partner to help facilitate any legal paperwork for you, such as your will or powers of attorney. Even if your medical outlook is hopeful and your support partner's health is excellent, it can be relieving for both of you to complete this task.

Communicating with your Children

✤ What to expect

The reality of recurring breast cancer or metastases can evoke a variety of responses from children. After your children watched you endure treatment the first time and saw that you recovered, their fears are often lessened and they are reassured. Your recovery from your initial treatment might have taught your children how strong you are. For other children, the recurrence of your breast

"I want to go back to the way it was before cancer."

cancer can make them see your vulnerability and test their sense of security.

It is natural for your children to have many reactions. Some children might minimize the seriousness of the recurrence or spread of your breast cancer. Your children might recall that you survived treatment before and expect the same results.

Some children might become angry. The recurrence of a traumatic event in their lives might test their tolerance limits. There might be a limit to how much your children can tolerate. They might reach a saturation point, lose patience, lack the ability to deal with the situation, and ignore dealing with your illness. Your children might become angry with you for being sick again and lack the maturity to realize that it is not your fault.

Depending on your children's ages, they might become anxious about who will take care of them if you cannot. If more than one caregiver is available for them, this worry might lessen. Similarly, your children might worry about who will take care of you.

Because they have experienced you going through treatment before, they might have a more realistic idea of what is involved. Your children will be better able to cope if they know that you have people to care for you and that they will not have to worry about you when you are ill.

Some children might be concerned if they are responsible for more work at home. Older children might be concerned about accepting household duties, or caring for younger children. Older children might also worry about finances or the absence of a parent's income. They might worry about not having enough money to continue sports or extra curricular activities or their education.

When dealing with breast cancer, at one time or another, many children share the fear of losing their parent. Children worry about how they will manage without their parent, and who will look after them. Support partners and family have a vital role to offer children balance and reassurance that they will be okay.

Listening to your children's distress can be difficult. You should share this responsibility with your partner and be aware of behavioural signals that might indicate distress. Do not assume that all your children's negative reactions are due to your breast cancer or family situation. It is natural for several other routine life events to trouble your children.

Remember that your children can handle the truth, if presented in a non-threatening, age appropriate manner.

❈ *What to do*

There is never a perfect time to share the information about the recurrence or metastases of your breast cancer, but keeping your children informed includes them in your life and experience. After you and your support partner understand your medical situation, share what you know with your family so that they can understand and prepare for how it affects them. Maintain control and decision-making between yourself and your support partner. Even though you are ill, your children need to know that you are still their parent.

After you tell your family, it will be easier for them to deal with their feelings in an open manner, instead of hiding them from you. Remember to talk to your children openly and honestly at an age-appropriate level. Keep the discussion open and ongoing, not just a one-time event. Also remember that you do not need to share every

"Be honest with your kids. Tell them the truth, let them digest the information, and then talk again."

concern or worry. It is perfectly acceptable to share the facts but to skip the details that do not affect them.

How you deal with your breast cancer affects how your children deal with it. In your communications, be aware that you set the tone for your children's reactions. In all your communication with your children, hope is an essential element. Just as you need something to hope for, so do your children. Your children might tell you that they think the disease will go away and that you will get better as you did when you were first diagnosed and received treatment. A statement such as this does not mean that they do not understand the seriousness of what you are telling them. They are simply letting you know that they love you and that they have hope for the future.

Encourage regular times for family discussions when everyone has the opportunity to talk about their feelings, both good and bad. Open discussion is a good strategy for encouraging communication in which each person's opinion is heard and valued.

Plan special times with your family. These times do not have to be expensive trips or days away from home, but activities that you can do together that everyone can look forward to. For example, you might want to implement a simple family routine of bedtime stories, movie and popcorn nights, or skating on the neighbourhood rink. These times can create memories and help your family remain close.

Acknowledge any help or efforts that your children offer and ensure that they maintain their schoolwork and outside activities. Try as much as possible to keep their routines intact.

If you are financially stable, reassure your children that they do not have to worry about any financial concerns. If you have financial burdens, decide what you need to share with your children so that they can plan accordingly.

Ensure that your children have trusted people that they can talk to. You might consider arranging family counseling through your Cancer Centre, your children's school, or your community. Group programs for parents or children who are dealing with a serious illness might be available in your area.

Respect that just as you need time to process the information, so do your children. Your will need time to adjust to the recurrence or metastases of your breast cancer and to process what this news means for them and how it affects their lives. Try to create a sense of security that does not wholly depend on you alone. Let your children know that you will make every effort to ensure that their needs are met at this time and in the future.

Recurrence or Metastases

Common concerns	• Cancer has recurred, come back, or spread • Need for more treatment • Cure might or might not be possible, depending on the circumstances • This stage of illness can be brief or extend over a period of years, resulting in chronic illness • Ongoing adjustment, flexibility, and acceptance is necessary • Increased anxiety and worry levels about the future
Parent with cancer	• Fear of fighting a losing battle • Loss of hope • Decreased capacity to parent and contribute to home life • Change in partner relationship • Might have more difficulty with treatment because of previous expectations • Side effects of treatment: nausea, hair loss, fatigue • Time away from work and financial worry
Support partner	• Fear that partner could die from illness • Loss of hope • Return to increased responsibility for children, household duties, and caregiver role to ill partner • Change in partner relationship • Caregiver stress and fatigue • Assist partner with completion of legal affairs • Financial worry

Children	• Need for information and for family routines to continue
	• Might dismiss or deny seriousness of the recurrence
	• Might readily accept these changes as familiar
	• Might appear to be uncaring and expect that their parent will respond to treatment as before
	• If illness continues, children might lose patience and hope, and may wonder when it will end
	• Need for patience, tolerance, and acceptance
Coping tips	• Understand in clear terms what your recurrence means
	• Communicate clearly with your children
	• Set realistic and attainable goals for yourself, your partner, and children
	• Accept the chronic nature of your illness
	• Take care of legal affairs
	• Accept help from others
	• Join a support group for yourself
	• Maintain hope
	• Continue to enjoy life and maintain family life as much as possible
	• Do what makes you and your family happy
	• Take it one day at a time

Recurrence or Metastases

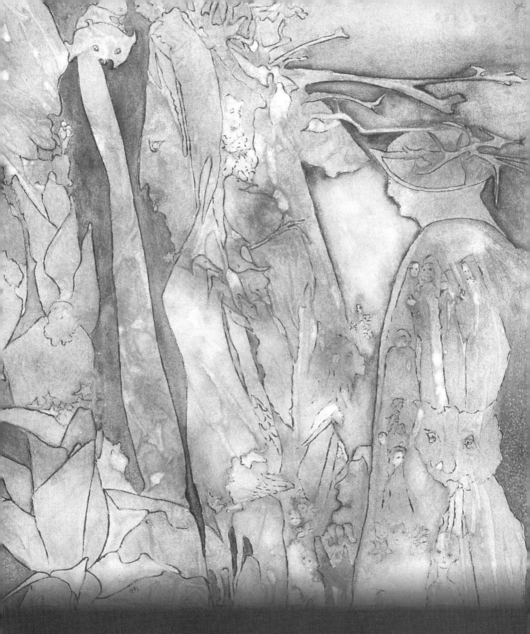

Legal Concerns

Legal Concerns

Taking Care of Yourself

> "Taking care of financial and legal responsibilities is important for all parents, regardless of their health."

❖ What to expect

All parents, whether healthy or diagnosed with a serious illness, need to think ahead and make provisions for the possibility that one or both parents could die before their children are independent. Planning for this possibility can be difficult because it involves thinking about your mortality. Thinking about your own death might be overwhelming to you. It might be upsetting when you think about how it can have an impact on your children. Some cultural traditions might not promote completing legal matters such as writing a will. If your illness advances to an untreatable state and death becomes likely, the need for such planning becomes even more important.

If you are a single-parent, child custody is an even more serious issue when you are ill and if your health worsens.

It is your responsibility as a parent to ensure that your financial and legal affairs are in order and that your wishes are clear and able to be implemented.

❖ What to do

You should take care of financial and legal planning as soon as you are able to do so. It is ideal to do as much of this planning as possible when you are in good health and have the

> "Take care of all the legal stuff as soon as you can. Then forget about it."

physical energy to do so. If you lose your mental capacity, you will not be able to sign legal documents, and if you become very sick, you might not have the energy to handle such matters.

Getting Support

❄ **What to expect**

Several legal services and financial options are available. Because specific legal terminology and precise details vary across Canada according to the laws of the provinces and territories, it is a good idea to seek professional advice to determine what is best for your family.

❄ **What to do**

You might be able to obtain advice free of charge or at reduced fees through several agencies, such as the following ones:

- Legal Aid
- A Legal Information Action Line in your community.
- Faculties of Law in universities
- Provincial and territorial ministries, such as the Ministry of the Attorney General in Ontario

It is very important for you to discuss your wishes with trusted family members or friends and to write them down so that they are clear if any disputes arise.

"Depending on your situation, legal issues can be complex."

"Seek professional advice on legal matters. It's worth doing right."

Making and Recording Legal Decisions

Guardianship

While your will can express your wishes regarding the guardianship of your children, your wishes for guardianship might or might not be implemented. You must designate legal guardianship to officially assign a guardian for your children. It is important to discuss guardianship for your children with your lawyer, especially if you expect any complications with your treatment.

In most two-parent situations, if one parent dies, the surviving parent continues the care of their dependent children. In their wills, all parents should name a potential guardian to look after their children until the age of majority in the event that both parents die. If no guardian is named, child guardianship becomes a legal matter that the courts decide. You should not assume that a family member, other than your children's other living parent, can or will automatically take over the care of your minor children should you become unable or should you die. You should discuss guardianship with your lawyer.

When you select a guardian for your children, you should consider the following issues.

Your children's best interests

A guardian's personal values and parenting style should be similar to yours and how you have raised your children. Your children should be familiar with and comfortable with this person. Guardians should respect your family heritage and their partners should also consent to being included in guardianship.

"Leave no unfinished business."

Guardian's age and physical and emotional health

A guardian should have both the physical and emotional energy to care for your children.

Guardian's geographic location

You should consider how far away a prospective guardian is from your children's extended family and friends, and whether they will make an effort to keep your children connected to their current support networks. You should also consider whether your children will have to change schools.

Guardian's financial stability

You should consider whether prospective guardians are financially responsible and whether they can afford to raise your children.

Guardian's consent

Naming a guardian in your will is not sufficient. While you are alive, you should address guardianship openly with the person that you want to name as guardian, as well as with your children. When you have chosen someone, you should get their express consent. Discuss the matter together in detail to ensure that the guardian is prepared to take on the responsibility and that you are satisfied with the guardian's approach to parenting before you name that person in a legal guardianship agreement.

Alternate guardian

You might also want to name an alternate guardian in case the first-named person is unable or unwilling to assume the responsibility when the time comes.

Make your wishes clear

Keep the person that you name as guardian informed about any specific wishes that you have for your children's future. For example, you might have concerns that your children stay together or that they use part of their inheritance for specific purposes, such as education or to travel to visit relatives. You should write down any wishes to be sure that they are known and clear.

Custodial concerns

If you are a single custodial parent, if you are a co-parent in a lesbian or gay relationship, or if you have serious concerns about the second parent's ability to care for your children, the issue of guardianship is more complicated. If this is the case, you should seek the advice of a lawyer. Appointing a guardian then becomes a decision for the courts. You can and should record your wishes in a guardianship agreement and make your concerns known to the potential guardian. You should complete a guardianship application as soon as possible, so that you can provide affidavit and verbal support for the application.

The court, however, will take the rights of a non-custodial parent into consideration when it makes a decision about your children's future care and custody. When you name a guardian, you should think of someone who would participate in a court challenge, particularly if you believe that the children could be at risk from their other parent.

Power of Attorney or Substitute Decision Maker

In Ontario, Power of Attorney is the term for the legal authority that you designate to another person to make decisions for you while you are alive, if you become incapable. In Ontario, this authority is separated between issues of personal care and issues of property. In other provinces across Canada, different legal terms might be used for this concept, such as a Substitute Decision Maker (SDM), and different provisions might apply.

Power of Attorney relates to decisions about your personal care and the management of your financial affairs and property while you are alive. Power of Attorney applies only while you are alive and allows you to retain a measure of control about what happens to you and to your property. You can name the person that you want to make decisions on your behalf and you can inform them about your wishes. In some cases, people designate persons other than their closest relative to act with Power of Attorney.

Power of Attorney does not apply to decisions about the care of your children now or in the future. Some people believe that by writing a will and naming an executor, that they have also named that person to make decisions on their behalf. This is not true. The executor in your will has no authority while you are still alive.

If you become incapable and have not designated a Power of Attorney for Personal Care, your next of kin is asked to make decisions. This might be your spouse, or if you don't have a spouse, your adult children could be asked to make medical treatment or personal care decisions for you. Prepare your family for these possibilities and discuss them. If you do not want your children over the age of 18 to be put in this position, you should designate someone else to be your Substitute Decision Maker (SDM). The decisions that an SDM makes should be according to your wishes, not according to their own values and beliefs. Your next of kin might not be able to make these decisions on your behalf. Make sure that the persons who are called upon to act as your SDM know and understand what you want if you are unable to make the decision yourself.

In Ontario, if you are deemed to be an incapable person and if you have not designated a Power of Attorney for Property, the Office of the Public Guardian and Trustee will assume responsibility for your financial affairs. Your next of kin will not be asked to make any decisions.

You should research whether Power of Attorney designation that is made without a lawyer is valid in your province or territory.

Living will or advanced directive

A living will or advanced directive provides more specific details about the care that you want to receive if you later become unable to express your wishes. Sometimes people write a living will or advanced directive, such as the University of Toronto's Joint Centre of Bioethics Living Will, that expresses their wishes for the medical care they want in particular circumstances, especially such issues as cardiopulmonary resuscitation (CPR), ventilators, or tube feeding. These wishes are usually very specific and can be incorporated in the document that designates Power of Attorney for Personal Care. You should discuss advanced directives with your physician to better understand what treatment options are available. Your lawyer can also help ensure that you phrase your wishes clearly.

All adults should consider designating a Power of Attorney to act in the event of accident or illness if they become incapable, even temporarily, of making decisions for themselves. Lawyers can help with Power of Attorney documents, or individuals can prepare the documents themselves. You can obtain kits with information and forms from the Public Guardian and Trustee, or a similar provincial body, or through your hospital or Cancer Centre social worker.

Wills and estate planning

Wills and estate planning are important practical considerations for your children's future. A will takes effect after your death and deals primarily with the dispersal of your property. Most people are aware of wills, but many people, however, avoid thinking about them because they are related to death. Keep in mind that if you die without a will, which is called intestate, the laws in the province where you reside decide how your estate is distributed. You and your family will have no say in this or in who should be named as the executor of your estate.

You should make a list of your personal effects and assets to let your family members know what plans you have made and where documents and other valuables are located.

Parents who are not legally married should investigate the laws that apply in your province regarding settling an estate where there is no will and one partner dies. For instance, unless there is a will or a legal contract between the partners, the surviving partner has no claim on property that the deceased partner owned, regardless of how long they have been together. Writing a will becomes even more important in such cases. Many people believe that without a will, there is a division of assets by unmarried spouses when one spouse dies. This is not true and this situation could cause anguish for your family if there is no will.

Estate planning involves writing a will, but is more inclusive. It refers to the use and distribution of your assets, and can involve how you manage these assets while you are still alive, as well as what you do with them after you die. There are different ways of passing assets to your beneficiaries, including giving gifts during your lifetime, setting up trusts, either during your lifetime or as a Testamentary

Trust after you die, and naming beneficiaries in your will for specific assets.

You should consult a reputable lawyer and estate planner, as several complexities can require legal advice. For example, Holograph Wills are wills that people write on their own, by hand, and sign. These types of wills might not be recognized in all provinces. The wording in these wills is often ambiguous and arrangements might be incomplete, so they can be held up in court for many months. Probate refers to a percentage of the value of an estate that goes to the province when an estate is settled. There is no such tax in Quebec. Often, people seek to avoid probate costs by reducing the value of their estate, such as by transferring their assets to their surviving spouse or naming individuals, rather than their estate, as beneficiaries of insurance policies, registered retirement savings plans (RRSPs), and so on.

You can set up trust arrangements to provide funds or assets for your children for specific purposes or at specific times. You can place money or assets into a trust fund that a trustee, who you select, administers. The trustee then disburses the money or assets when certain conditions are met, such as when the children reach a certain age.

The Henson Trust is one such arrangement that is designed specifically for parents to pass their assets to their children who have physical or mental disabilities and who might never be able to manage their financial affairs entirely independently. You should discuss this particular type of trust with a legal advisor who is familiar with it. If you are a parent of a child with a disability and if your own health is vulnerable, a Henson Trust arrangement might help ensure that your child receives government benefits after your death.

Communicating with your Children

"What will happen to us if you die?"

✤ What to expect

Your children will likely worry about what will happen to them if you die.

The plans for your children's care if you die might be obvious to you and your partner, but children lack the experience and maturity to assume what you take for granted. Your children need reassurance that they will be safe and cared for by people who love them and want the best for them. They might also worry about their own health and the health of others close to them. You should reassure them that this is normal, and also assure them of the health and safety of those around them.

✤ What to do

If your children are old enough to understand, talk with them about the arrangements that you have made for their care. State the obvious to them. If the children will stay with your partner after your death, tell them. Reassure your children that they will be well cared for after you die. Be prepared to go over the arrangements several times so that they understand. Explaining these plans will show them that you are concerned about them and provide them reassurance that they will not be left on their own. Although it is not advisable to leave the choice of a guardian to your children, it might be a good idea, depending on their age, to get their reactions to plans that you are considering.

"When the whole family is on the same page, no one feels left out or excluded."

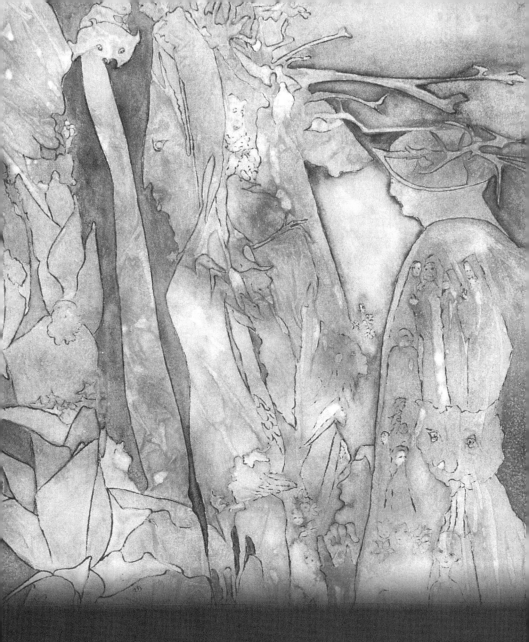

Advancing Illness and Dying

Advancing Illness and Dying

Taking Care of Yourself

✤ What to expect

At some point in your journey with breast cancer you might hear the news that your cancer has continued to advance, that treatment cannot control it from spreading to the rest of your body, and that you might have only a limited amount of time to live. Even if you have prepared yourself for this possibility, it is always devastating news for you and your family.

Learning that your illness is irreversible and that you might die from it is difficult for many reasons, but partly because of the uncertainty that surrounds it. Even your doctor who delivers this news might not use the words "death" and "dying." You and your family members might be left to draw your own conclusions. But if your doctor does mention death, your immediate question is likely "How much time?"

You might not want to know how long you have to live or you might want to ask about a time frame so that you can plan ahead. Many factors affect predictions of how long people can live with an advancing or terminal illness. At best, doctors can only give a rough estimate of the time that you might have left.

Although you might have been told that there is no cure for your breast cancer, you might

"The cancer has spread and the medicine is not strong enough to treat it."

feel well with little or no pain. If this is the case, you can continue to live and enjoy life with your family. If you need help with pain and symptom management, you can ask your physician to refer you to a palliative care or pain specialist. Advances with medications and services mean that many cancer patients can continue to enjoy activities at this time.

Dealing with advancing illness involves uncertainty and many ups and downs for you and your family. This is a profoundly significant time, and it is different for everyone.

❀ *What to do*

If your doctors tell you that you have a limited time left, you should try to live as fully as possible. Many breast cancer patients who are facing incurable illness have continued to participate fully in their family's lives for many months. Although your natural instinct might be to withdraw, it is still important to focus on life, maintain the best quality of life that you can, and to live as well as you can in the time that you have. If you keep your emphasis on living, and not dying, you can help yourself and your family members come to terms with the reality of the situation.

Facing death and preparing for it does not mean that you have to give up hope. Hope can mean many things for many people and what you hope for might change over time. This is a special stage of life when living in the moment has exceptional meaning, because time becomes very precious.

Place your emphasis on living as fully as possible, with the awareness that your life is going to end before you, your partner, or children want it to end.

Make practical decisions about your end of life care, including where you prefer to die.

"Maintain hope and continue to enjoy life."

These decisions might depend on your family circumstances, the amount of care that you need, and the support services that are available in your community. When you talk with your health care team, be sure that they understand what you want for your future care. Ultimately, these decisions should be yours and those of the adults who will share your care. Discuss your wishes with others so that they know what you want and can help you make decisions. Even if you have preferences and make plans accordingly, be aware that unforeseen events might change them.

Ask about which of the following resources are available in your community:

- Palliative care providers

- Home care

- Additional support at home

If necessary, ask your health care team for any referrals. This information can help you plan, even if you do not need to make a decision immediately.

Think about where you want to spend your final days:

- At home

- In a hospice

- In hospital

If you are thinking about spending your final days in the familiarity and comfort of your own home, you should consider the following questions:

- Will your family be comfortable with the situation?

- Are enough people available to care for you?

- Is relief available for your caregivers?

- Are caregivers available for your children?

- Can your home accommodate a hospital bed and other medical equipment, likely in the main living area?

- Are medical personnel, such as your family doctor, palliative care physician, or nurses, available to visit you at home?

- Are you and your family comfortable with the potential loss of privacy in your home as a result of health care professionals and visitors being present?

If you are thinking about spending your final days in a hospice, you should consider the following questions:

- Is a hospice available in your community?

- Do you prefer to have palliative care physicians and nurses readily available?

- Are you comfortable being separated from your family?

- Are caregivers available for your children?

- Are you and your family comfortable with the potential loss of privacy as a result of being in a more public environment?

If you are thinking about spending your final days in a hospital, you should consider the following questions:

- Do you prefer to have palliative care physicians and nurses readily available?

- Do you have a health situation that requires specialized treatment?

- Are you comfortable being separated from your family?

- Are caregivers available for your children?

- Are you comfortable with strict guidelines for visiting hours?

- Are you and your family comfortable with the potential loss of privacy as a result of being in a more public environment?

Regardless of where you prefer to spend your last days, talk to your loved ones about what you want to happen when you are near death. You might want to think about and let others know how little or how much you prefer to be medicated to manage pain or other symptoms. Also, let people know if you have preferences for medical intervention. For example, if someone calls 911, the paramedics that respond are obligated to undertake resuscitation procedures. You might want to research or consider Do Not Resuscitate orders.

If you have not already done so, you should complete all legal matters such as drafting a will, making financial decisions, assigning Power of Attorney, and designating legal guardianship for your children. These legalities can be very difficult to think about, but they are important responsibilities for all parents.

As illness advances, you should also collect and make available important papers such as the following documents:

- Will
- Social Insurance Number (SIN) card
- Provincial health card
- Medical benefits cards
- Birth certificate
- Marriage certificate
- Insurance policies
- Details for an obituary, such as names and birthplaces for you and your family members
- Personal wishes for funeral and burial arrangements.

Advancing Illness and Dying

Getting Support

✤ What to expect

An advancing or terminal illness can cause manypeople to reflect on their lives, and on their spiritual needs and issues. Whether or not you follow a particular faith, you might want to address these issues with the help of a religious or spiritual advisor.

As your illness progresses, you might become too ill or exhausted to parent. This process might be gradual, or a sudden decline in your health might make you need to transfer your parenting tasks sooner. Handing over parenting tasks might be difficult for you and your partner, and might cause tension as roles change. This shift of responsibilities does not mean that you love or care less for your children.

This will be a very difficult time for your support partner, too. Partners have to manage the demands of increased caregiving responsibilities for you, your children, and your household at the same time as coming to terms with the thoughts of living life without you. Your support partner might need to take a leave of absence, stress leave, or vacation time from work and might want to claim Compassionate Care Benefits. Your support partner, as well as your friends and family, will likely experience stress, anxiety, sadness, anger, guilt and frustration. Anticipating loss is very difficult, and everyone will need support.

✤ What to do

If death is likely in the near future, you should begin sharing or handing over your parenting jobs. Accept help from your friends and family. Try to set up a support system for you and your

"Maintain hope and continue to enjoy life."

"It helps to surround yourself with strong and positive people."

family to help with responsibilities such as co-ordinating appointments, running errands, organizing meals, doing laundry, car pooling, and providing child care.

You might save emotional and physical energy if you appoint one person to pass on your health information to other friends and family members. You can ask someone to send regular updates to share information about your medical situation, so that you can avoid the emotional burden and have more time to spend with your family.

Seek professional counseling. Ask your health care team for services available for you and your children. Family counseling or group programs that offer professional or peer support can help ease the stress of this time.

Take time to talk to your support partner, and others who are close to you, about your hopes and future dreams for your children and those around you. These are emotionally difficult issues, but it is better to discuss them openly instead of keeping them inside and believing that you can spare yourself and your loved ones the pain that is associated with dying. Being open and honest can be emotionally draining, particularly at a time when your physical resources might be declining, but it can be comforting to share these feelings. You and your partner might benefit from outings, such as times when you can just enjoy the present and not think about the future.

Ensure that your support partner and caregivers are taking care of their own health, that they have someone that they can talk to and rely on, that they are continuing to do the things that they enjoy, and that they are maintaining as much of their normal routine as is possible.

"Spend whatever time you have wisely."

Communicating with your Children

❖ What to expect

When your children become aware that you will not get well, everyone in the family will begin to experience anticipatory grief. As a parent, you can help your children by showing your feelings openly, and by talking about your sadness and anger. Assure your children that their feelings are normal and show them how to express their feelings in a healthy way; for example, by writing, drawing, or engaging in physical activity. It is natural to be tearful and to cry about what is happening. You cannot make the pain disappear, but you can make it easier to deal with by being open and honest about it.

It is natural for your children to be sad and uncertain about what will happen to you and to them. Your children might experience fear over the following issues:

- Being alone with you while you are ill

- Being responsible for dealing with an emergency in your health

- The uncertainty of the future

- Who will care for them

- Their own health

- A surviving parent's health

Do not be surprised if your children ask about the process of dying. They might be interested in the physical process of how your body shuts down and dies. On the other hand, they might want to avoid this information and discussion altogether. Or, they might be curious, but uncomfortable asking direct questions.

"There may not always be answers, but there is always love."

Children of all ages will have difficulty maintaining sustained focus on your anticipated death without a rest. The pain of living with a dying parent might become too much for your children, at times. Your children might want and need to spend more time with friends or relatives to manage their stresses. At the same time, they might feel guilty about spending time with their friends or having fun. Reassure them that you are happy when they are having a good time with others, and that their happiness is okay with you.

As you delegate and shift your parenting tasks, your children might find that things are not done the way that you did it. This can add to the burden of their adjustment. Talking about these changes can help to smooth any transitions. Endorsing your partner's efforts can make them more acceptable to your children.

Remember that your children still need your attention. While all this activity is happening, it is sometimes hard to remember that there are times when you and your children need to spend some time together, when they have your full attention.

❧ *What to do*

As with any stage of your breast cancer, when you communicate with your children, you should be honest and open with them. It is distressing to tell your children what is happening to you, but sharing feelings openly and honestly, and discussing the future, can help children be more open about death. If you maintain open communication, you encourage your children to express their feelings, which can help them come to terms with your death and their grief. You might feel that you need help from your support partner, a good friend, family member, or health professional to talk about this.

"Cherish every moment that you have."

Advancing Illness and Dying

Helping your children understand that your breast cancer is likely going to end with your death is best done in a gradual process. By giving the news in stages, you can give your children the opportunity to gradually understand that you are dying. First, make sure that your children understand that you cannot get better because the treatment is no longer working. Then, explain that your health is getting worse. Finally, inform them that you will get too sick for your body to live, and that you will die. Your children might want to know what to expect as your disease progresses. Giving factual information and being willing to answer questions might help lessen your children's fears.

You can also investigate the possibility of having a family medical conference in which your children can meet members of your health care team. This can be very helpful for clarifying any misunderstandings and explaining your illness in plain language. Your children might ask questions and receive information about your illness from your physician directly. By this experience, your advancing illness might become more real to them. A family medical conference might help your children understand your breast cancer and its progression and might also better prepare them for what lies ahead.

When you talk to your children about death and dying, talk about it as a natural part of life. Let your children know that you are sad that you will not be there later to share the milestones in their lives. You can grieve this loss together. This anticipatory grieving can help your children express how they feel while you are still an active part of their lives and gives you the chance to reassure them that their lives will go on. Let them know that you understand that they will be saddened by your death, but that you believe that they will be able to manage this loss with the help of the supportive people around them.

While these types of discussions can be very emotional, they can make grieving easier for your children after your death. These conversations can also bring you closer to your children.

Tell your children how you want them to react to your death, so that they have an idea of how to grieve. Let them know that it is okay to experience sadness and happiness after you are gone. You might want to share your thoughts with your children to help them understand your personal spiritual beliefs, and what you believe about life and death. Your culture and spiritual tradition might offer useful ways to deal with the loss of a loved one.

Depending on the age of your children, you might want to share your thoughts about the possibility of your partner developing a new relationship at some time after your death. This discussion might help avoid difficulties later. Giving permission to your surviving partner to develop a relationship after your death might help your children accept a new person in your partner's life because you have given approval and shared this with them. Also, give your children permission to allow other people into their lives, such as a step-parent, and give them permission to be loved by that person. Explain that loving someone else does not mean that they do not love you.

Help your children, especially older children, identify who they can go to for support. These people might be inside or outside your family and should be adults who are interested in your children and who are not so closely involved in the grieving. They might be professionals from your children's school, religious community, health care team, or family friends.

Find resources for your children. Look for age-appropriate books, videos, or tapes that help explain terminal illness and dying to children.

Advancing Illness and Dying

Reading can give your children information that they can return to when they want and can demonstrate examples of other children who have experienced the death of a parent. This information can help them make sense of and validate their feelings and your family situation. Child-centered resources help everyone understand that the feelings expressed by children when a parent is dying are normal.

Try to maintain a normal routine, but prepare your children for changes that affect them. Your children need to know how your advancing illness and dying will affect their everyday life in the family. Continue to live and to enjoy each day with your children. Make every effort to tell them that they give you great joy and comfort, and communicate your love to them. Birthdays, holidays, and special days will remain important to your family, so try to celebrate them as normally as possible. Remember that you are modeling ways for your children to cope with difficult times in life and that you are creating memories and offering your children lessons in living.

Questions and Answers

Your children might have questions. Answer them as honestly as you can. If you do not know the answer, tell your children you will try to find out. Your children might not be able to put these questions into words or they might not feel comfortable asking them out loud. They might need answers to the following difficult questions.

- **When are you going to die?**

  Your children need to know that even when death is very close, no one can predict when it will happen.

- **Where are you going to die?**

  Talk to your children about your choices and preferences for where you want to spend your last days and what you think it might mean for them. There are benefits and challenges for you and your family to weigh. For example, if you remain at home, they can see you often, but they can also see your health deteriorate and might see you die. If you are in a hospice, they are able to visit, but might not see as much of you or your partner, and they will need alternate childcare. The same applies in a hospital, where there might be less privacy.

- **What happens when you die?**

  Depending on your own comfort level and on your children, you can tell your children what the doctors have told you will likely happen as death approaches.

- **Who will care for you when you are sick?**

  If you stay at home, your children might wonder who will look after you. In the absence of information, they might wonder if they will be responsible for your care. Tell them what to expect, and who will be caring for you at different times. As your illness progresses, at all times, you will need a trusted adult to be your primary caregiver. If adolescents and young adult children will assume some caregiving responsibilities, they will need an adult to call. Be careful not to give too much responsibility to a willing son or daughter. Everyone requires respite from the demands of caregiving.

- **Can I visit you when you are sick?**

  Children can visit you in a hospice or hospital, although in hospitals there might be more restrictions on visiting hours. It is important to tell children what to expect when they visit. They might notice the changes in your appearance, or that you are sleeping and not ready to have a conversation with them. Arrange for them to be accompanied by an adult who can comfort them about the visit, if necessary. If you are admitted for symptom management, the visiting experience might be different from being admitted because death is near. If you are unconscious, your partner or another adult should explain your condition before your children see you, to reduce the shock. It will help your children if they know whether they can touch or hug you and talk to you.

If you are at home, your children might want to make brief visits to your room. If you are in hospital, you might rely on a friend or relative to bring them for visit. For younger children, visits should be brief and older children will let you know how long they want to stay.

If your children want a break from hospital or hospice visits, respect their wishes if possible.

- **What do I need to do?**

  Children might not know what to do or how to help while a parent is dying. It might help to give them a job or task according to their age and interest so that they can be involved, such as reading you a story, watching TV together, or running an errand. Your caregivers might be able to offer direction.

  Your children will also need a break from the situation. You can help by planning regular breaks for your children away from home. You can join the outing if you are feeling well, or it can just be time away from the family for your children, visiting friends or family. Take your cue from your children as to what to do.

- **What will happen in the case of an emergency?**

  Try to ensure that your children are not left alone to care for you. Plan ahead with your children for possible emergency situations, and update the plans regularly so that you all know how to get help if needed. Keep a list of phone numbers for family and friends who your children can call for help if necessary. Even a very young child can be taught how to call 911. Give guidance about calling 911. Remember that doing so commits

  paramedics to taking resuscitative actions that you might or might not want to happen. If you are at home, have your wishes in writing.

- **Who will look after me during an emergency?**

  Share your childcare plans with your children, and your children's school, in case of possible emergencies or changes in arrangements.

- **How will I remember you?**

  You might choose to prepare a reminder or keepsake for your children. You might want to start by telling your children about their family history. Their history might include their cultural heritage and the meaning of certain family traditions. These stories can help connect your children to their past, their present, and to you. You could put images, photos, gifts, or mementoes together to create a memory book or box, a tape recording, or a video of your thoughts. You might want to assemble a collection of items that your children can keep and remember you by. Find a medium that is most meaningful and least stressful for you.

  You might want to share some of the following messages with your children:

  - I will always love you.
  - I want you to be happy.
  - You might feel sad when you think of me, but this will get better in time.
  - Remember the good times that we shared.
  - I believe you will grow up to live a good life, and be a good person.
  - I want you to follow your dreams and hopes for the future.

  You might want to take a memorable family trip, take a family portrait, or create memory boxes that hold special mementos for your children as they grow. Sharing messages and memories can bring you closer to your children, and can let them remember these feelings in future years. The value of your bond with your children comes from the power of your relationship and attachment that you forge in the years that you spend together.

- **Will we be able to say goodbye?**

  Even if your death does not seem imminent, your children need an opportunity to say goodbye. As much as everyone wants death to be peaceful and planned, this is not always the case. If you were to die suddenly, due to a complication, your children might not have the opportunity to say goodbye. Encourage your children to express themselves in written or art form, if they are comfortable with this. Even very young children can do that.

  If for some reason you die without saying goodbye to your children, there might be other ways for them to say goodbye to you. One possible suggestion might be a message that your children write on a piece of paper. Your children can read the message aloud, place it in your casket, or make it into a paper boat and release it into a river.

Advancing Illness and Dying

Advancing illness and dying

Common concerns	• Illness is advancing with no hope of control • Pain and symptom control • Dealing with dying • Time is limited
Parent with breast cancer	• How and when will you die? • How do you tell your children? • How will your family manage without you? • If a single parent, how will you manage? • Where do you want to die? • Worries about your children and the added demands on your support partner
Support partner	• Facing life without your partner • How does your family continue under this stress? • Work and money worries • How can you cope with your role of caregiver? • Where will your partner decide to die? • Who can support you at this time? • If a single parent, how will you manage
Children	• Continuing need for information • Continuing need to have a caring adult presence • Need time and support to understand that their parent can die in the near future • Fear of loss of parent • Fear of what will happen to them • Will benefit from knowing plans for care in the event of their parent's death • Do not want friends to treat them differently • Want life to be normal

Coping tips	• Hope for the best and prepare for the worst
	• Live life as fully and as well as you can
	• Seek out sources of strength such as complementary therapies, palliative care, and spiritual support
	• Connect with your support partner
	• Handover parenting duties
	• Plan family outings when you feel well
	• Be open and available to your children
	• Enjoy simple things as a family
	• Express your love and affection for your family
	• Complete financial and legal arrangements

Advancing Illness and Dying

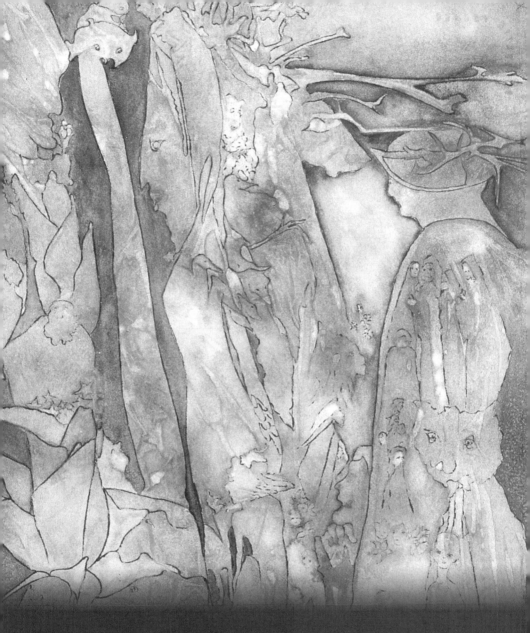

Death and Grieving

Death and Grieving

Taking Care of Yourself

❊ What to expect

The physical process of dying is different for everyone. It might happen suddenly or, more likely, your health might decline over a period of time as your illness progresses. You might experience increased sleepiness, decreased eating and drinking as your bodily systems function less, and maybe some restlessness. Gradually, you will have less awareness and contact with those around you. You might slowly withdraw into your own world where your concerns are more important than those of your family. This does not mean that you care for them any less; it is just that you have your own journey to complete. You might want to seek spiritual care at this time, alone or with your family.

In many societies, death and dying are taboo subjects. The mention of serious illness and death often makes people feel uneasy, and we prefer to avoid talking about it even when it is happening to those close to us. Avoiding pain and sadness can make your illness more difficult for you and your family.

The similarities between birthing and dying have been observed many times. Both are times of caring, tension, and anticipating an event. The major difference is that one brings joy, the other sadness.

"We are all on loan to each other."

It is incredibly difficult to conceive of your death or to tell someone that you are dying. Death can

115

connote different things for different people, including the following ideas:

- Facing the end of your life
- Exhausting all treatment options to control or cure your disease
- Worry about your children and how they will manage without you
- Taking care of unfinished business in your life
- Fearing pain, and wondering whether it can be controlled
- Losing strength and physical abilities
- Being confined to bed
- Understanding that your future is limited
- Watching people avoid or separate from you while you are still living and need them
- Leaving your loved ones and your family
- Celebrating a well-lived life with loved ones
- Becoming closer to your spiritual beliefs or making a spiritual transition

For many, death and dying mean dealing with all of the items above. Regardless of what dying means to you, the concept is both sad and frightening for you, your partner, and your children.

❋ What to do

Think about how you want your family to recognize your death. Consider whether you want a religious ceremony according to your spiritual tradition, or a less formal celebration of your life. Share your wishes for your funeral arrangements so that they are understood and can be respected by your family. Take the needs of your children and loved ones into consideration when you make these plans.

"The question is not whether we will die, but how we will live."

Some people feel that they do not want a funeral or memorial service for themselves. Before making a decision, you should talk to your family and consider their feelings and grieving processes. Most religious and cultural traditions have a ritual that acknowledges death. These rituals vary in form, but usually serve to recognize both the life of the deceased person and the loss of those who are bereaved and need to grieve.

If you do want a service, it might be in keeping with your religious or cultural traditions, or might be a service that you plan to reflect your life or personality. These services can be either solemn or joyful occasions where family and friends comfort one another.

A funeral service can be arranged in a place of worship or a funeral home chapel, with your body present, and can be followed by burial or cremation. A funeral service is usually held within a few days of the death, but can be delayed to allow family to arrive.

A memorial service is held when the body is not present, such as if it has been buried, cremated, or donated for medical research. A memorial service is most often held within a few days or weeks of the death. Memorial services, like funeral services, can be large or small, joyful or solemn and can be held in a place of worship, funeral home, chapel, hotel, or family home.

Direct disposition is the term used when there is no funeral or memorial service and the body is taken directly to a crematorium. You might also want to consider the following issues in advance:

- Whether you prefer your body to be buried, cremated, or donated for medical research

- Whether you prefer to have an open casket

- Whether you have a preference for the clothing or items to be buried with your body

- Whether you have a preference for organ donation.

- Where you prefer your body to be buried or have your ashes scattered

- Whether you would like to contribute to a newspaper announcement or obituary

- Whether you have a favourite photograph that can be published or displayed at a service

- Whether you would prefer flowers or memorial donations to a specific charity

Getting Support

✤ *What to expect*

Your death will be a very difficult, stressful, emotional, and busy time for your loved ones.

After you die, a doctor must sign a medical certificate of death, wherever the death occurs, whether at home or in a medical setting.

When you die, your support partner might want to contact a minister of your faith for any spiritual care that is usual for your religious or cultural tradition.

You support partner or caregiver will have to contact a funeral home, which they can do at any time of day or night, and the home will make arrangements for your body to be moved to the funeral home. If not previously arranged, someone will need to visit the funeral home to make decisions, which will vary with different spiritual affiliations.

"It's under-standable to feel overwhelmed."

After the funeral or memorial service, the funeral director will provide your family with the following documents:

- Proof of Death certificates
- Forms with which to claim death benefits from Canada Pension Plan, if applicable

❊ What to do

As soon as possible after the service, your family should do the following things:

- Make arrangements to pick up any of your personal belongings from the hospital or funeral home, if applicable.
- Supply your bank with a death certificate and copy of your will so that the bank can close accounts and make any transfers.
- Complete paperwork for Canada Pension Plan (CPP) for survivor and child benefits, and any life insurance or Old Age Security (OAS) that you had.
- Contact a lawyer to set probate in motion.
- Contact any other financial institutions, such as insurance companies.
- Cancel any of your memberships

To cope with your death, your support partner and your loved ones need to remember to do the following things:

Ask for help. The time immediately following a death is very busy. Your loved ones will need to determine which responsibilities are theirs and which tasks someone else can do.

Conserve energy. Delegating tasks can help your loved ones conserve energy to be with your children, and handle the emotional times that lie ahead.

"Take it one day at a time."

Maintain routines. Your loved ones should try to maintain their daily routines as much as possible.

Take time. The people who supported you will need time to absorb the shock of your death. They might need to take time to be by themselves and take a break from all of the people who are trying to comfort them.

Grieve. Your loved ones will need time and space to mourn, either on their own or with friends and family. It takes time and courage to grieve and to recognize and cope with difficult feelings. Grieving is a process of gradually coming to terms with a loss. It does not happen all at once. People grieve at their own pace, which should not be hurried. Your loved ones also need to realize that time is not enough. They need to work through their grief by attending to their feelings and acknowledging their loss. Grief is an experience, not an issue to fix or solve.

Seek solace in spiritual or cultural traditions. These traditions might provide your loved ones with rituals and ways to express their grief. Planning a funeral that is in keeping with your values and beliefs might assist your loved ones to express the sadness and emptiness that they feel.

Communicating with your Children

❧ *What to expect*

Your death might be your children's first experience with death. If your children are present when you die, they will know that you have died. If not, they will need to be told. Your children might want to see your body, either in the hospital or at a funeral home. Children might

"I miss you and wish you were here."

be frightened and will need the presence and support of a parent or caring adult to accompany them to see your body. However, if your children do not want to see your body, your support partner and family should respect their wishes.

Grieving at any age means working through difficult feelings after the loss of someone you love. Children grieve in different ways, according to their age, developmental stage, and unique personalities. Many bereavement experts believe that children start to understand death between the ages of seven and nine but that they are not fully able to process the death of someone close to them until they are in their teens.

Children might regress in their behaviour and emotional responses during stressful times. They might act out with aggression or turn inward and withdraw from their usual connections. Children's concentration and attention span at school and other activities might become shorter and they might also display physical symptoms such as stomach or headaches. This is normal, as long as it does not continue for an extended period of time.

Young children might turn to fantasy and play to express their feelings and fears after the death of a parent. They might or might not ask questions. Younger children might act as though nothing has happened and might not appear to be aware or might seem numb. They might look as though they forgot about this major event and go on about their business of play and activity as usual. This is not unusual and might be their way of coping with a difficult situation that is too much for them to handle right away. Some children might become more attentive toward adults, become clingy, and ask questions about their health and safety.

Many children will experience fear after a parent dies, but they might not speak openly about them. Some common fears include that they will forget you, that their remaining caregiver will get sick or that they might become sick.

Some children might mistakenly think that they caused or contributed to their parent's death. Some children might express anger that their parent has left them. Without knowing how to express this anger directly, they might behave inappropriately. They might be ashamed of their angry feelings. Sometimes children wish that their other parent had died and feel guilty about this.

Teens might not readily display their grief within the family, but instead might talk to their friends more openly. This can also apply with younger children.

Some children might not be able to or will not express any grief until they feel that the adults around them can handle it.

As the adults and caregivers around your children deal with their own grief, your children might need more help than they can give them at this time. There might be bereavement groups for children held in their area. Professional help can be accessed through their doctor, from a school guidance counselor, a social worker, or psychologist who can help your children deal with their grief. If your children experience a change in their school performance, or if they show signs of anxiety over an extended period of time, such as refusing to go to school, inability to sleep, or a loss of appetite, they should have professional help.

❖ What to do

Even if your children were told that you were going to die, your death might still come as a shock to them. Your children need to understand what death means, and using proper terms about death can help. People who discuss death with your children should avoid terms such as "gone away" and "gone to sleep" as these can be

"Children learn by observing adults."

confusing and possibly frightening, especially for younger children.

If death happens suddenly, or was not previously discussed, this might be the first time that your children talk about it. Explanations about death should be simple and brief; children will ask for clarification when they are ready. Your family's spiritual and cultural experience can often help to explain death.

Children need to know that death is a natural part of life, that all living things die, and that it is permanent and irreversible. Dead people no longer feel anything. They do not feel pain. They do not walk, talk, breathe, eat, or sleep. This might or might not be beyond your children's age and understanding. Most importantly, your children need to understand that while death is final and irreversible, it is still possible to remember you and to keep a special place for you in their hearts and memories.

Your children can better deal with your death and their grief if the adults around them are in touch with their own grief and deal with it in a healthy way. Watching others gives them a way to understand their own grief and also gives them permission to grieve.

Your children should be invited to all ceremonies and services of remembrance and should have an opportunity to say goodbye to you. It is important for children to have the opportunity to participate and to express their feelings. Do not assume that services will be too difficult an experience for your children. They should have the choice to attend. Children are resourceful and have the capacity to handle these situations when shown the way.

Either you or a loved one should explain to your children what will happen to your body after you die, such as whether you will be buried or cremated, whether you will have a funeral or memorial service, and the details of what will happen at the event.

In addition to funeral rituals, children can also benefit from more personal family remembrances of their parent who has died. Continued remembrance encourages them to preserve memories for the future. Your friends and family members should continue to talk about you and can help your children remember you by celebrating your birthday, anniversary, or other special events.

If your children were unable to express certain things to you while you were alive, their caregiver should help them find ways to express these things. Children need the opportunity to express their sadness and anger. They need to know that negative feelings are normal, that they lessen over time, and that grieving helps heal the pain so that life can continue. Some hospitals and hospices have grief programs for children where they can work out their feelings by talking and sharing or through art or play therapy. Many children also benefit from active play or sports, where they can release energy and anger. Creative play, such as drawing or playing with dolls or action figures can also help children work through emotions.

Children's feelings need to be acknowledged, but they also need limits for appropriate behaviour.

More than anything, your children need to be encouraged to go on with their life and to follow their dreams. Your children should also be reassured that you would want them to continue to live, have fun, laugh, and experience new things.

Death and grieving

Common concerns	• Pain and suffering • Saying goodbye • Sadness and loss
Parent with breast cancer	• Concerns about a painful death • Preparation for death physically, spiritually, emotionally • Pain and symptom control • Dying with dignity • Worries about not being ready to die • Guilt about leaving children and family
Support partner	• Feelings of shock and numbness • Exhaustion • Multiple burdens of caring for dying partner, caring for children, preparing for a funeral or service • Maintaining daily routines • Feelings of relief, sadness, guilt, loneliness, anger • Concerns about being alone and being a single parent • Financial worries
Children	• Need to know that they are loved and that caring adults will take care of their needs • Need to learn ways to express their grief and will model positive adults in their life • Need opportunities to take a break from their sorrow • Worry that friends will treat them differently • Might not know how to handle attention or messages of sympathy from others

Coping tips

- People need to let themselves grieve and express their sadness
- Children should continue to hear about and remember their parent
- Those who are grieving should spend time with friends and relatives who can provide a listening presence
- People need distractions to escape their grief temporarily
- Grief should not disconnect the surviving parent from the children
- Try to maintain routines
- Consult with teachers and activity leaders about how children are coping
- Spiritual supports and rituals can help with grief
- Engage in simple activities with your children to release physical tension and allow for normal activities
- Consult your health care team for professional bereavement help for yourself or your children if you are having trouble coping

English Resource list

This selection of resources may be helpful to you and your family when looking for information about life with breast cancer. There are suggestions for books and videos that may be found in your Cancer Centre or public library, and a listing of reliable websites about the illness, treatment and side effects, information for partners and caregivers, talking to children and books for children to read. Some resources may only be found in specialized library collections.

General and Treatment Information

- **100 questions and answers about breast cancer.** Zora Brown. Jones & Bartlett, 2002

- **Bosom buddies: learn, laugh and live through breast cancer.** Rosie O'Donnell & Deborah Axelrod. Warner, 1999

- **Breast cancer: a guide for patients.** Pamela Chart, Coles Notes Medical Series 2000

- **The breast cancer survival manual: a step-by-step guide for the woman with newly diagnosed breast cancer.** John Link, Cynthia Forsthoff & James Waisman. Henry Holt and Company, 2003

- **Breast cancer: the complete guide.** 4th. ed., Yashar Hirshaut and Peter Pressman. Bantam, 2004

- **Dr Susan Love's breast book.** 3rd ed., Susan M Love, Perseus, 2000.

- **Intelligent patient guide to breast cancer.** 3rd ed., Ivo Olivotto, Intelligent Patient Guides, 2001.

- **Understanding breast cancer: general and clinical levels (CD-ROM).** Princess Margaret

Hospital, University Health Network. Jack Digital Productions, 2001. (Try your Cancer Centre library for this one)

- **What you need to know about breast cancer: diagnosis, treatment and beyond.** Pat Kelly & Mark Levine. Key Porter Books, 2002.

- **Your breast cancer treatment handbook.** Revised 6th ed., Judy C Kneece. EduCareInc.com. 2004.

Treatment

- **100 questions & answers about your cancer and cancer treatment side effects.** Joan Kelvin. Jones and Bartlett, 2004

- **After mastectomy: healing physically and emotionally.** Rosalind Benedet. Addicus Books, Omaha, Nebraska, 2003.

- **Coping with chemotherapy.** Nancy Bruning. Avery, 2002

- **The breast reconstruction guidebook: issues and answers from research to recovery.** Kathy Steligo. Carlo Press. San Carlos, CA, 2003

- **Initial discovery and diagnosis of breast cancer.** Woman to Woman: a video series for breast cancer patients; Media Arts Associates Inc. 2001. (Try your Cancer Centre library for this one.)

- **Living in the postmastectomy body: learning to live in and love your body again.** Becky Zuckweiler, Hartley & Marks, 1999.

- **Making decisions about the removal of my breast cancer: what do I prefer?** Institute for Clinical Evaluative Sciences, 1998. (Try your Cancer Centre library for this one.)

- **Surgical choices.** WomenStories: a video series for breast cancer patients. Women Stories 2003. (Try your Cancer Centre library for this one.)

- **Understanding lumpectomy: a treatment guide for breast cancer.** Rosalind Dolores Benedet & Mark C. Rounsaville. Addicus Books, 2003.

- **Woman to woman: a handbook for women newly diagnosed with breast cancer.** Hester Hill Schnipper Joan Feinberg. Avon Books, 1999

- **Woman to woman: breast cancer and reconstruction options: a discussion for any woman diagnosed with breast cancer.** Bosom Buddies Inc. Bosom Buddies, 1998.

Personal experiences

- **Breast cancer: landscape of an illness.** Penelope Williams. Penguin Group (Canada) 2004.

- **Hope is contagious: the breast cancer treatment survival handbook.** Margit Esser Porter. Simon & Shuster 1997.

- **Just get me through this! A practical guide to breast cancer.** Deborah A. Cohen & Robert M. Gelfand. Kensington Publishing Corp. 2000.

- **Stories of hope and healing: six women confront breast cancer.** Leslie E. Strong. Equinox. 1994.

- **That other place: a personal account of breast cancer.** Penelope Williams. Dundurn Press. 1993.

- **Uplift: secrets from the sisterhood of breast cancer survivors.** Barbara Delinsky. Simon and Shuster, 2001.

For Young Women

- **Fighting for our future: how young women find strength, hope and courage while taking control of breast cancer.** Beth Murphy. McGraw-Hill, 2003.

- **I'm too young to have breast cancer! : regain control of your life, career, family, sexuality and faith.** Beth Leibson-Hawkins. Lifeline Press 2004

- **Young women and breast cancer** (video). WomenStories, 2003. (Try your Cancer Centre library for this one.)

After Breast Cancer

- **After breast cancer: answers to the questions you're afraid to ask.** Musa Mayer. O'Reilly, 2003.

- **After breast cancer: a common-sense guide to life after treatment.** Hester Hill Schnipper & Lowell E. Schnipper. Bantam Books, 2003.

- **After cancer: a guide to your new life.** Wendy Schlessel Harpham. New York: HarperPerennial, 1995.

- **Dancing in limbo: making sense of life after cancer.** Glenna Halvorson-Boyd and Lisa K Hunter. San Francisco : Jossey-Bass, 1995.

- **Ladies in waiting: a play about life after breast cancer.** Toronto Sunnybrook Regional Cancer Centre, 2002. (Try your Cancer Centre library for this one.)

- **Living beyond breast cancer: a survivor's guide for when treatment ends and the rest of your life begins.** Marisa C Weiss & Ellen Weiss. Times Books, 1997.

Partners

- **100 questions and answers about caring for family or friends with cancer.** Susannah L Rose and Richard T Hara. Jones and Bartlett, 2005

- **Breast cancer husband: how to help your wife (and your husband) through diagnosis treatment and beyond.** Marc Silver. Rodale, 2004

- **Cancer in two voices.** Sandra Butler and Barbara Rosenblum. Spinsters Ink , 1996

- **Caregiving : a step by step resource guide for caring for the person with cancer at home.** Peter S Houts & Julia Bucher. American Cancer Society, 2000.

- **Couples confronting cancer: keeping your relationship strong.** Joy L Finannon and Katherine V Bruss. Atlanta : American Cancer Society, 2002

- **Facing cancer : a complete guide for people with cancer, their families and caregivers.** Theodore A. Stern & Mikkael A. Sekeres. McGraw Hill, 2004

- **Helping your mate face breast cancer: tips for becoming an effective support partner.** Judy C Kneece. Columbia : EduCare Publishing, 1995

- **Intimacy. Woman to Woman Breast cancer series.** Medical Media Associates, 2001 (Try your Cancer Centre library for this one.)

- **It takes a worried man.** Brendan Halpin. New York : Villard, 2001

- **No less a woman: femininity, sexuality and breast cancer.** Deborah Hobler Kahane. Hunter House 1995.

- **Pebbling the walk: surviving cancer caregiving.** Steve Reed. Portland, Oregon: Blue Heron Publishing, 2000.

- **Sexuality and cancer: for the woman who has cancer and her partner.** American Cancer Society, 2001. (free booklet available from the Canadian Cancer Society)

- **A significant journey: breast cancer survivors and the men who love them.** American Cancer Society,1997. (Video)

- **Spouse to spouse: what it's like when your partner has cancer.** Oncology Nursing Society and Cancervive. Video. (Try your Cancer Centre library for this one.)

- **Ties that bind: when your partner has breast cancer.** Oncology Nursing Society and Cancervive. Video. (Try your Cancer Centre library for this one.)

- **When the woman you love has breast cancer.** Chicago : Y-ME National Breast Cancer Organization, 1997. (also online at www.y-me.org)

Talking to Children

- **Breast cancer: a family survival guide.** L Pederson and J Trigg. Westport: Bergin & Garvey,1995

- **Breast cancer online: in our own words: how we told our children.** Breast Cancer Action Nova Scotia, 2001. (available online at www.bcans.org/booklets/index.htm)

- **Can I still kiss you?: Answering your child's questions about cancer.** Neil Russell. Health Communications Inc. 2001.

- **Cancer and the family.** Lea Bader. New York: Wiley, 1996

- **Cancer in the family: helping children cope with a parent's illness.** Sue P Heiney. Atlanta: American Cancer Society, 2001.

- **Helping your children cope with your cancer: a guide for parents and families.** Peter Van Dernoot. Long Island, NY, Hatherleigh Press, 2002.

- **How to help children through a parent's serious illness : supportive, practical advice.** Kathleen McCue. New York: St Martin's Griffin, 1996

- **We can cope: when a parent has cancer.**
Newton: Inflexxion Inc, 2002. Set of 3 video
tapes (for parent, teens and child) and
guidebook (Try your Cancer Centre library for
this one.)

- **When a parent has cancer : a guide to caring
for your children** (includes Becky and the
worry cup for children). Wendy S Harpham.
New York: Harper Collins, 1997

- **When a parent is sick: helping parents
explain serious illness to children.** Joan
Hamilton. East Lawrencetown, NS: Pottersfield
Press, 2001

Resources for teenagers and older children

- **My Parents Cancer.** If you are a teenager and
have a parent with cancer, we have developed
a website just for you
www.myparentscancer.com

- **Afraid to ask: a book for families to share
about cancer.** Judylaine Fine. New York, Beech
Tree Books, 1986

- **Hear how I feel** (video – 25 min). Northeastern
Ontario Regional Cancer Centre 1996. (Try your
Cancer Centre library for this one.)

- **Moms don't get sick.** Pat Brack. Aberdeen, S
Dakota: Melius Publishing Co, 1990

- **The year my mother was bald.** Ann Speltz.
Washington: Magination Press (American
Psychological Association), 2002. (Try your
Cancer Centre library for this one.)

For children 5-10 years

- **Becky and the worry cup (in when a parent
has cancer: a guide to caring for your
children).** Wendy S Harpham. New York:
Harper Collins, 1997

- **Can I still kiss you? Answering your children's questions about cancer.** Neil Russell. Deerfield Beach, Florida: Health Communications Inc, 2001

- **Good luck, Mrs K!** Louise Borden. New York: Margaret K McElderry Books, 1999 (when a teacher has cancer)

- **The hope tree: kids talk about breast cancer.** Wendy Harpham. New York: Simon & Schuster, 1999

- **I know I made it happen : a book about children and guilt.** L Blackburn. Omaha: Centering Corporation, 1990

- **Kids tell kids what it's like ... when a family member has cancer** (video – 30 min). Cancervive, 1998

- **Once upon a hopeful night.** Risa Sacks Yaffe. Pittsburgh: Oncology Nursing Press, 1998

- **Our mom has cancer.** Abigail and Adrienne Ackerman. Atlanta: American Cancer Society, 2001

- **The paper chain.** Clare Blake. Santa Fe, Health Press, 1997

- **Time for me: an activity book for kids when someone in the family has cancer.** June Slakov. BC Cancer Agency, 1999. (phone 604-930-4000 to buy a copy)

- **Vanishing cookies: doing OK when a parent has cancer.** Dr Michelle B Goodman. Downsview, On: Benjamin Family Foundation, 1990

- **When Eric's mom fought cancer.** Judith Vigna. Morton Grove, IL: Albert Whitman & Co, 1993

For young children

- **Once upon a hopeful night.** Risa Sacks Yaffe. Pittsburgh: Oncology Nursing Press, 1998

- **Our mom has cancer.** Abigail and Adrienne Ackerman. Atlanta: American Cancer Society, 2001

- **The paper chain.** Clare Blake. Santa Fe, Health Press, 1997

- **Time for me: an activity book for kids when someone in the family has cancer.** June Slakov. BC Cancer Agency, 1999. (phone 604-930-4000 to buy a copy)

- **Vanishing cookies: doing OK when a parent has cancer.** Dr Michelle B Goodman. Downsview, On: Benjamin Family Foundation, 1990

- **When Eric's mom fought cancer.** Judith Vigna. Morton Grove, IL: Albert Whitman & Co, 1993.

Recurrence or metastatic disease

- **Advanced breast cancer: a guide to living with metastatic breast cancer.** 2nd ed. Musa Mayer. O'reilly and Assoc. 1998

- **At the waters edge: when cancer comes back.** Alberta Cancer Board/Breast Cancer Info Link, 1998.

- **Handle with care? : living with metastatic cancer.** (Videorecording) Toronto Sunnybrook Regional Cancer Centre. 1998 (Try your Cancer Centre library for this one.)

- **Recurrence and metastasis** (video recording). Buffalo N.Y. WomensStories, 2003

Advanced illness

- **The dying time: practical wisdom for the dying and their caregivers.** Joan Furman & David McNabb. Random House Inc. 1997

- **Facing death in the family: caring for someone through illness and dying, arranging the funeral, dealing with the will and estate.**

Margaret Helen Kerr & JoAnn Kurtz. John Wiley and Sons. 1999.

- **Final gifts: understanding the special awareness, needs and communication of the dying.** Maggie Callanan & Patricia Kelley. Poseiden Press, 1992.

- **Handbook for mortals: guidance for people facing serious illness.** Joanne Lynn & Jan Harrold. Oxford University Press, 1999.

- **Living with the end in mind: a practical checklist for living life to the fullest by embracing your mortality.** Erin Tierney Kramp. Three Rivers Press, 1998.

- **Stay close and do nothing: a spiritual and practical guide for the dying at home.** Merrill Collett. Andrews McMeel Publishing, 1997.

Websites

National organisations

- **Canadian Cancer Society.** Source of factual and supportive information for patients and their family. www.cancer.ca, www.ontariocancertrials.ca

- **Canadian Health Network** General health information from Health Canada www.canadian-health-network.ca

- **Clinical Trials.gov** Information from the National Institute of Health (US) about all types of clinical trials. www.clinicaltrials.gov

- **MedlinePlus** from the US National Institute of Health, links to reliable sources of general medical and drug information. Includes interactive slideshows. www.nlm.nih.gov/medlineplus

- **National Cancer Institute.** (US) Comprehensive site with treatment, support and clinical trials information on all types of cancer. www.cancer.gov

- **National Center for Complementary and Alternative Medicine.** Information about complementary medicine, including clinical trials, from the US National Institute of Health agency. www.nccam.nih.gov

Provincial Organisations

- **Cancercare Ontario.** Includes links to the provincial Drug Formulary and Clinical Practice Guidelines. www.cancercare.on.ca

- **OntarioCancerTrials.ca** Information on clinical trial being undertaken in Ontario, www.ontariocancertrials.ca. A collaboration of the Canadian Cancer Society and the Ontario Cancer Research Network www.ocrn.on.ca

- **BC Cancer Agency** Includes information about Unconventional Therapies. www.bccancer.bc.ca/default.htm

Breast Cancer Websites

- **Canadian Breast Cancer Foundation.** CBCF works collaboratively to fund, support and advocate for: relevant and innovative research; meaningful education and awareness programs; early diagnosis and effective treatment; and a positive quality of life for those living with breast cancer. Has a wide selection of diagnosis and treatment information viewable at this site. www.cbcf.org

- **Canadian Breast Cancer Network.** National network of breast cancer survivors, includes site for young women with breast cancer. www.cbcn.ca

- **Breast Cancer Care.** Information and resources from the UK includes information for young women and explanations of metastatic (secondary) disease. www.breastcancercare.org.uk

- **National Breast Cancer Centre.** Information and resources from Australia, includes information about metastatic disease and information for teenagers. www.nbcc.org.au

- **Y-ME National Cancer Organization.** Information and resources from US, includes information for partners and regular teleconferences on breast cancer related subjests. www.y-me.org

- **Ontario Breast Cancer Information Exchange Partnership.** Links to many local Ontario breast cancer information and support organizations can be found at this site. www.obciep.on.ca

- **Breast Cancer Action Ottawa.** Local breast cancer support centre, programs include meetings, aquafit and exercise classes. www.bcaott.ca

Advanced Cancer

- **American College Physicians Home Care Guide for Advanced Cancer** – This online resource provides helpful and reassuring information for those with advanced cancer and the people caring for them. Information about dealing with various symptoms and when to seek professional assistance, how to include children at this time, dying and grieving. www.acponline.org/public/h_care/index.html

French Resource List

Information générale

- **Cancer du sein: ce que vous devez savoir.** Pat Kelly, Mark Levine. Traduction de: What you need to know about breast cancer. Laval: Guy Saint-Jean, 2004.

- **Bien manger pour mieux vivre : conseils diététiques pour la personne en traitement contre le cancer.** Montréal: Fondation québécoise du cancer, 6e éd. rév., 2004. (Les guides de la Fondation québécoise du cancer).

- **Tant d'histoires autour des seins** [ensemble multi-supports]. Collectif. Montréal: Planète rebelle, 2003. Livre et CD.

- **Tout savoir sur le cancer du sein.** John R. Lee, David Zava et Virginia Hopkins. Vannes: éditions Sully, 2002.

- **Vivre pendant un cancer.** Marie-Paule Dousset. Paris: éditions Seuil, 1999.

- **Quand la maladie grave survient s'informer, comprendre, agir.** Dallaire Michelle, Mongeau Suzanne. Régie régionale de Montréal-Centre, Direction de la santé publique, 1998.

- **À bout de patience - Les enjeux de la lutte au cancer du sein.** Sharon Batt. Montréal: Les Éditions du Remue-ménage, 1994.

Traitements

- **Les prothèses mammaires.** Laurent Benadiba. Paris: éditions Estem, 2001.

- **Se reconstruire face à un cancer du sein.** Jeannette Jehane. Paris: éditions Chroniques sociales, 2000.

- **Le cancer du sein sans mutilation.** Roger Poisson. Montréal: éditions du Méridien, 1997.

- **Le cancer du sein et autres maladies du sein.** June Engel. Laval: Guy Saint-Jean, 1996.

Témoignages et expériences personnelles

- **L'urgence de vivre.** Louise Potvin. Outremont: Publistar, 2004.

- **Ma victoire sur le cancer du sein : vue avec les yeux du coeur.** Malenfant, Danielle. Saint-Antonin: Merlin, 2003.

- **Le combat de ma vie: si je vieillis, c'est que je suis en vie.** Dominique Dufour et Lise Giguère. Outremont: Publistar, 2002.

- **Ces femmes au sein blessé.** Betty Hania. Parie: éditions Le Félin, 1993.

Romans et récits

- **Une femme sur dix.** Catherine Roig. Paris: Plon, 2004.

- **Le jeu de l'oie: petite histoire vraie d'un cancer.** Sylvie Desrosiers. Montréal: Les éditions La courte échelle, 2003.

- **Le défi de l'amour.** Diane Gagnon. Québec: Arion éditeur, 1998.

Comment parler aux enfants

- **Hôpital silence.** Nicole Landry-Dattee et Marie-France Delaigue-Cosset. Paris: Calmann-Levy, 2001.

- **Ces enfants qui vivent le cancer d'un parent.** Nicole Landry-Dattée. Paris: Ed. Vuibert, 2005.

Pour les enfants, à partir de 6 ans

- **Le voyage de Luna.** Diane Barbara et Frédérick Mansot. Actes Sud, 2002.

- **Puce.** Brigitte Ventrillon et Pierre Mornet, Autrement jeunesse, 2001.

- **Un dragon dans le coeur.** Sophie Leblanc, Beauport: Publications MNH, 1997. Ce livre est épuisé chez l'éditeur mais il est disponible à la Fondation québécoise du cancer. Vous pouvez l'emprunter en téléphonant au 1-800-363-0063 ou en allant sur le site Internet de la Fondation, au Centre de documentation virtuel, à l'adresse: www.fqc.qc.ca.

Pour les enfants, à partir de 8 ans

- **Histoire de Josée.** Marguerite, Gouin. Montréal: éditions Paulines, 1992.

Pour les jeunes, à partir de 12 ans

- **Lettres à Félix.** Welsh, Renate, Paris: Hachette, 1991.

- **J'ai douze ans et je ne veux pas que tu meures.** LeShan, Eda Joan, Paris: Bayard, 1992.

Après le cancer du sein

- **En pleine forme après un cancer du sein : exercices essentiels de guérison du corps et de l'esprit.** Sherry Lebed Davis. Traduction de: Thriving after breast cancer. Boisbriand, QC: éditions Momentum, 2003.

- **Conseils et exercices suite à une chirurgie pour le cancer du sein.** Vidéocassette. Animé par Josée Lavigueur. Produit par Virage et Norvartis, 2002.

Maladie avancée

- **Promets-moi de le dire: portrait d'une femme exceptionnelle qui s'offre le rendez-vous ultime avec elle-même.** Judith Larin. Montréal: Stanké, 2003.

- **Trouver l'espoir face à la mort.** Christine Longarer. Paris: éditions J'ai lu, 1997.

- **Accompagnement au soir de la vie.** André Gauvin et Roger Régnier. Montréal: éditions du Jour, 1992.

Sites Web généraux

- **Fondation québécoise du cancer.** www.fqc.qc.ca. Les publications de la Fondation sont disponibles gratuitement sur ce site.

- **Fondation du cancer du sein du Québec.** www.rubanrose.org/fr/

- **Réseau québécois pour la santé du sein.** www.rqss.qc.ca/rqss/. Témoignages et documents vidéo en ligne. Liste de ressources régionales. Forum d'échange.

- **Réseau canadien du cancer du sein.** www.cbcn.ca/french/. Liste de publications, ressources et liens.

- **Sunnybrook and Women's College Health Sciences Centre** (Toronto). www.femmesensante.ca/. Site en français.

- **Ligue nationale contre le cancer** (France). www.ligue-cancer.asso.fr

- **Essentielles.net.** Site d'échange dédié aux femmes atteintes du cancer du sein. www.essentielles.net/

Sites Web régionaux

- **Région de Montréal:** www.ompac.org/, www.santepub-mtl.qc.ca/ (Dir. de santé publique de Montréal), www.viragecancer.org (Bibliothèque de livres, vidéos et enregistrements)

- **Région de Québec:** www.pages.globetrotter.net/oqpac/

- **Région du Saguenay:** www.cbcn.ca/sentiernouveau/

- **Région du Nord du Québec:** www.cbcn.ca/afleurdesein/

- **Région de l'Est du Québec:** www.aceq.org

- **Région de l'Estrie:** www.rosedesvents.com

Acknowledgements

The saying goes that it takes a village to raise a child. In this case, it took a whole village to write this book. I cannot express the depth of my gratitude to the people and organizations listed below. When I first proposed taking the wisdom learned in our "What about my kids?" workshop, I had no idea what a journey it would be, and how many people would join me along the way.

The Village

The Project Managers

These are the people who individually dedicated their time and talent to the book:

- Rosemary Williams, the first project manager and Maggie Tabalba, who shared their energy and passion for making this resource a reality for family, by contributing writing and editing expertise.

- Rosemary Farrel, the second project manager, who stepped in and helped move the project through a transition phase.

- Lois Crowe, who came on board in January 2004, and who kept this project on target and helped bring it to reality.

The Editors

- Louise Rachlis generously gave her time and expertise with the support of her employer, the Ottawa Citizen.

- Kim Hicks, a freelance editor, provided editing services.

- A special thanks is given to Amy Laird who provided the final edit that helped bring this resource to life, giving it a focus, clarity and a "voice" for parents.

The Artists

- Chris Marin, a freelance artist, generously donated the original artwork for the cover and each of the chapters.
- Tamara Annis created the graphic icon used for the focus group posters.

The Illustrators

- Jennifer West provided invaluable insight for illustrations, text formatting, and style to make the words stand out and the resource easy to use.
- Francine Boucher, who took our ideas and created the unique design and layout for the book.

The Francophone Group

Many people contributed their skills and expertise to ensure that the French version of this book reflects the needs of the Francophone communities. Un gros merci à Huguette Asselin, Stephanie Austin, Jean-Luc Bourdages, Ghislaine Daze-Belisle, Linda Durocher, Dr. Paul Genest, Manon Gosselin-Hebert, Marie Claude Jean, Lucie Kearns, Liane Murphy, Dr. Marie Pelletier, Dr. Lucile Robillard, Joceline Thibodeau, Monique Yelle

Thanks to our translator Valencia Léger, and French editor Dominique Fortier, for a superb French version of the book.

The Original Project Committee

Debbie Gravelle, Diane Manii, Gail MacCartney, and Christine Penn, all provided support, expertise, and encouragement. Diane Manii's experience with the "Living for Today" support group provided insight for the chapter related to metastatic breast cancer. Christine Penn collected and prepared the invaluable resources section for this book. Jane Lorente Shepherd and Christine Sones gave their voices and support from the beginning of this project.

The Reviewers

This book also benefits greatly from the insights and suggestions of the following people who freely gave their expertise and help by supporting and reviewing it at different stages in the process of production: Shauna Adeland, Marisa Akow, Joan Auden, Dr. Sarah Calleia, Dr. Mario Cappelli, Beth Collison, Serena Corsini-Munt, Abebe Engdasaw, Ron Ensom, Dr. Mary Jane Esplen, Diane Ford, Cathy Gilpin, Dr. Carolyn Gerin-Lajoie, Barbara Goodwin, Louise Haley, Elizabeth Kent, Margaret Lerhe, Sheryl Luxembourg, Dr. Gerald Munt, Kenneth Pope, Dr. Lucille Robillard, Christine Sones, Jane Lorente -Shepherd, Jennifer Williams, Barbara Newport, Nora Ullyot and Pamela Grassau.

A special thank you to Dr. Eva Tomiak who gave considerable time and expertise in reviewing the book many times, and making sure that the medical and genetic statements were accurate and appropriate.

The Funders

This project was made possible with the generous support of the following institutions and community partners:

- This project made possible with the generous support of the Canadian Breast Cancer Foundation – Ontario Chapter.

- Ottawa Regional Cancer Foundation

- St. Matthew High School, Bear Hug Fund Raiser, and The Force (Patrick McNulty and Monique Amyot)

- Social Work Department of The Ottawa Hospital Regional Cancer Centre

The Community Partners

Our partners contributed their support and insight in creating this project and in helping run the focus groups.

- Canadian Cancer Society Reach to Recovery Program (Deborah Dean)
- Breast Cancer Action (Anita Bloom)
- Ottawa Women's Breast Health Centre (Genevieve Cote)
- Arnprior and District Breast Cancer Support Group (Elta Watt)

The Focus Group Participants

We ran several focus groups (in English and French) in an attempt to make this book as relevant as possible to families. The participants included:

- Parents with breast cancer
- A partner of a parent with breast cancer
- A friend or family member who helped care for children of a parent with breast cancer
- A child whose parent has or had breast cancer
- People working with those who have breast cancer

This book has truly been a cooperative endeavour.

Profound thanks to all,
Linda J. Corsini